D1212229

John
Jacob Astor

Young Trader

Illustrated by Gray Morrow

John
Jacob Astor

Young Trader

By Dorothy S. Anderson

THE **BOBBS-MERRILL** COMPANY, INC.
A SUBSIDIARY OF HOWARD W. SAMS & CO., INC.
Publishers • INDIANAPOLIS • NEW YORK

To

Donald

Illustrations

Contents

CHILDHOOD
OF FAMOUS
AMERICANS

★ ★

John

Jacob Astor

Young Trader

A Lost Sister

It was 1770 in the little German village of Waldorf. Seven-year-old John Jacob Astor sat up in his bed. He sat up so quickly that the feather quilt slipped onto the floor. The church bells were clanging loudly.

John Jacob glanced at his brothers' beds. They were empty!

"What's wrong?" called John Jacob.

There was no answer.

He jumped onto the floor and pulled on his black breeches. He hitched red and yellow suspenders over his sturdy shoulders. Then he ran out into the courtyard.

Across the courtyard from the Astor cottage was Poppa Astor's butcher shop. John Jacob's blue eyes sparkled with anger as he hurried. He wondered why his brothers hadn't called him. They had promised to call him that morning!

John Jacob poked his blond head into the shop. No one was there.

He listened to the church bells once again. They were clanging loudly indeed. "Something must be wrong," he thought. John Jacob knew the bells were rung to warn the villagers of storms or trouble.

He heard his stepmother come into the courtyard. Mama Astor looked worried.

John Jacob shouted to make himself heard over the noise of the bells, "What's wrong, Mama?"

Mama Astor wiped her red eyes with a corner of her full apron. "It's your sister Maria. She must have arisen before everyone and gone out alone. She's lost!" cried Mama Astor.

"Can't anyone find her?" asked John Astor.

"The villagers have looked nearly everywhere. They've almost given up hope."

John Jacob stood as tall as he could. He tried to comfort his stepmother. "Don't worry, Mama. I'll find Maria," he declared.

"You?" Mama Astor shook her head. "Your big brothers have looked everywhere. No, you stay here, John Jacob. Then you won't get lost, too. You go stay in the front room of the cottage, with Catherine and the baby."

John Jacob thrust out his lower lip.

Mama Astor sat down by the butter churn. She let her head slump down on her hands.

John Jacob walked slowly toward the cottage. "No one thinks you can do anything when you have three older brothers!" he thought.

In the front room eleven-year-old Catherine was trying to stop baby Lisbet from crying. Catherine was crying all the while herself.

13

"Don't be so sad," said John Jacob. Tears gathered in his own eyes as he thought of three-year-old Maria by herself. He shook his head hard. He didn't want anybody to see him cry.

Suddenly John Jacob snapped his fingers and exclaimed, "I remember now that Maria and I were playing in the forest yesterday. Maybe she went to the same place again. I'm going to look for her."

"No, no!" said Catherine. "George and Heinrich and Mel have looked everywhere. You must not get yourself lost, too."

John Jacob protested, "Grownups never know the secret places where children play. I'm going to find Maria!"

Saying no more, he ran out the door into the main street of the village. His heart beat loudly as he ran over the cobblestones. He ran past the church. The bells were still clanging.

Near the village school he almost bumped into

14

a horse. Any other day he would have stopped to look the horse over, but today he ran on.

Housewives were washing clothes by the village pump.

The blacksmith's wife called to John Jacob, "We were out looking all morning. There's no use in your looking, too."

Another woman warned John Jacob that wild boars and evil spirits must have captured Maria in the forest.

"I'm not giving up!" said John Jacob, shaking his head. He ran on to the old Roman road at the edge of the village. His feet clapped on the smooth pavement that the soldiers of ancient Rome had laid down.

"John Jacob!" called some farmers looking up from their rye fields. John Jacob's short legs moved faster, carrying him away until he could no longer hear the farmers' voices.

He looked about for a tiny head of blond curls.

15

The only bright things he saw were the flowers and butterflies in the meadows.

"Maria! Maria!" he called. Then he stopped and listened for an answer. He called so loudly that he was sure he could be heard as far as the Rhine River. There was no answer.

John Jacob plunged into the thick beechwood forest. The trees were so close that their branches twisted together overhead. Little sunlight came through. Some of the trees were so short they looked like dwarfs.

The ground was matted with sticks and leaves, and John Jacob's feet made no sound as he walked. "I couldn't hear Maria if she was walking close by," he thought.

The day before, he had marked the trail that he and Maria had followed. He had done it by bending down twigs. Now he followed the twigs. He bent more to make the trail clearer. "Maria!" he called. His voice sounded spooky. A cold wind swept through the forest. John Jacob shivered, but he hurried on.

He looked overhead. None of the branches just above had been pushed aside. It was clear that none of the grownups had looked here. "Thank goodness I came!" he thought.

The trail led to an old wall. It was three hundred years old, and most of it was in ruins. John Jacob knew it was fun to walk on top of the wall but dangerous for a three-year-old.

Up ahead, the ruins formed a tiny room. Maria and he had played in the room the day before.

John Jacob climbed forward and looked inside. There was Maria sound asleep. Her cheeks were rosy, and her mouth was blue from eating too many berries.

John Jacob dashed into the room so fast that he knocked a stone away from the wall.

Maria awoke with a start. When she saw John Jacob, she smiled and hugged him. Excitedly,

17

she took an old coin from her apron pocket and said, "Look! I found it for you, John Jacob!"

He gazed down at the old coin. Then he rubbed it on the bottom of his black breeches. The coin was too old to sparkle anymore.

"It's an old coin the Romans left," said John Jacob. "They must have left it when they built roads through this part of Germany." His older brothers also had found coins and parts of jars that the Romans had left.

John Jacob led Maria away from the ruins. "Walk behind me, Maria. I'll follow the trail home." He held a thorny branch aside.

"Do you know the way, John Jacob?"

"Poof!" he said. "I can find my way." He watched for the twigs he had bent. Maria walked slowly. They came upon a stump blocking their path. John Jacob lifted Maria over it.

"I'm tired!" said Maria as she flopped onto the base of the stump. She rubbed her small hand over the green moss on its side. "Um-m! It's soft," she said with a smile.

"The moss is good for something, too," said John Jacob. "When you're lost in the forest, you can tell which way is north. You just look at the side of a tree the moss is on. There is much to learn about the forest, and I want to learn all I can. Come on, Maria."

Just as the children came to the edge of the forest they heard a low grumbling sound.

Maria put her trembling arms around John Jacob. "Maybe it's a wild boar!" she cried.

"No," laughed John Jacob, "it is thunder."

"Oh, dear! It'll rain."

"Maybe it won't rain at all," replied John Jacob. Even as he spoke, drops pattered down on the leaves of the trees. He looked worried.

"Anyway," said Maria, from beneath a tree, "it's safe and dry under all the trees."

Jacob knew it was not safe at all. Maybe lightning would strike! He took his sister's chubby hand and hurried across the meadow.

In spite of the storm, the streets were crowded with villagers.

"Thank the Good Lord you're safe!" said Granny Schmidt as she wrapped a dry cloak about Maria.

The schoolmaster was there, and the pastor, and the mayor. The cartwright had come out so fast he still held a brand new wheel in his hands. The whole village seemed to be there.

It was hard to get past the crowd to the Astor place. Everyone was glad that Maria was safe.

Outside the butcher shop, so many members of the family rushed out to hug Maria that they bumped into one another.

Poppa Astor stood in the doorway, his butcher's apron about his big waist. Eighteen-year-old George swung John Jacob up onto his shoulders.

Happiness shone on Frau Astor's face. "When

John Jacob wants to do something, he does it," she said. "He sticks to what he's doing, even though he's the smallest of the boys."

"We're proud of you, son," said Herr Astor. "You must think of something you want. You shall have a reward."

It took John Jacob no time at all to think of his wish. "Please, Poppa," he said as he leaned down from George's shoulders, "I want to work! Let me work in the butcher shop!"

A Sausage Trader

"STUFF-STUFF-STUFF." John Jacob's song rang through the butcher shop. His round head bobbed back and forth as he worked. Sitting on a bench, he could look out the door into the courtyard. He didn't let himself do much looking, however. There was too much work to be done. He had sausages to make.

First he opened an empty sausage skin. He scooped a fat fistful of sausage mixture from a wooden bowl. He stuffed it down into the skin. He pinched the skin to make a link. Then he started on the next sausage in the link.

"Working is fun," he thought. He looked up

to see if his big brothers had noticed how hard he was working. No one was looking though. Everyone was much too busy with his own work.

In one corner of the shop was a wooden chopping table. There Poppa Astor, Heinrich, and Mel were chopping up big pieces of meat. Mel's real name was Melchior. He was twelve years old and tall and strong. He wanted to be a farmer and raise crops.

Heinrich was sixteen years old and plump like Poppa. He wanted to be a butcher.

Behind a counter, Mama and Catherine were mixing sausage meat in a big wooden bowl. John Jacob smelled the spices they were using.

Poppa Johann Jacob Astor's first wife, Maria Magdalena, died when John Jacob was three years old. Poppa then married a woman whose name was Christina Barbara.

John Jacob sang louder. Only Maria noticed. She was playing out in the courtyard.

Hans Schmidt, John Jacob's playmate, poked his freckled face through the doorway. He was eating a piece of fresh pumpernickel bread.

"I worked all morning helping Granny with her baking," said Hans. "Now I'm going to play out by the mounds. Why don't you come, too?"

At the edge of Waldorf there were several fine mounds. John Jacob and his friends thought that it was fun to stand at the head of a mound and pretend to be sailing a great ship on the ocean—sailing to a distant land.

John Jacob stuffed one whole sausage before he answered. "I can't," he said. "I have work to do. I'm very busy."

"You've been working and working and working!" pleaded Maria, who was now standing next to Hans. "Come and play with us."

"I'll give you a bit of pumpernickel if you come," offered Hans.

John Jacob's mouth watered. With all the

butchering work to do, Mama and Catherine had no time to bake.

John Jacob glanced toward his big brothers. "No, Hans, I can't come," he said. "I'm too busy today!" Proudly, he held up the string of sausages for Hans and Maria to see.

Maria's eyes grew wide with wonder, but Hans only laughed.

John Jacob's face became hot and red. "What's the matter?" he asked.

Hans held his stomach. He was laughing so hard that the words came out in gasps. "Your sausages are so—so lumpy and—bumpy looking. They look like—stuffed stockings!" He turned and ran.

John Jacob's face grew redder and hotter. He bit his lip to keep his temper. Even now none of his brothers had looked up.

"Poppa, why is there so much work to do now?" John Jacob asked in a loud voice.

"It's harvest season," said Poppa Astor. "Every farmer needs meat salted or smoked or made into sausages. Salting and smoking keep it from spoiling. It is the custom here to have the meat prepared at harvest time so that there will be meat to eat throughout the winter."

John Jacob kept stuffing sausage.

Poppa shook his head and sighed. "The farmers around Waldorf are not rich enough to eat meat often," he said. "That's why we sometimes have no work at all, except at harvest time. A butcher barely makes a living here." He looked up. "Well, how are you doing, John Jacob?"

Mel and Heinrich set down their meat choppers and came with Poppa to see John Jacob's work. They turned the sausages over and over. Finally they straightened up.

"Good work," said Poppa, patting John Jacob's shoulder. "Good work!"

"Well done," said Heinrich. "You'll make a good butcher some day."

John Jacob smiled at the praise. He was not sure that he wanted to be a butcher when he grew up, but he was sure that he liked to work.

An ox-cart clattered on the cobblestones outside. John Jacob heard whistling.

"It's George!" cried John Jacob. He jumped up and ran out of the shop. He helped George

28

carry in a big piece of meat. He whistled a tune along with George.

When John Jacob and George had finished their tune, Catherine clapped her hands and said, "I'd say John Jacob is as good in music as George is. Maybe when John Jacob grows up, he will want to work in music, too, as George wants to."

Mel turned to John Jacob and asked, "What do you say you want to do?"

"I don't know," said John Jacob. "I just want to work."

John Jacob noticed now that Mama Astor was looking over his sausages. His forehead wrinkled with worry. Mama Astor was not easy to please.

"They are not bad for a beginner," she said in an ordinary tone.

"Look at the last sausages he stuffed," Heinrich said holding up a string of linked sausages. "The last ones are as good as any of ours."

Mama nodded. "Yes," she said, "but we cannot sell these first three sausages to any of our customers. We will have to replace them, and no one will want these."

John Jacob could see now that the first three he had done were lumpy.

"We could eat them ourselves," suggested Heinrich. "The meat is good."

Frau Astor said with a sigh, "It's not more meat we need for the meal. Already we have the scraps and extra bits of meat from your chopping." She shook her head. "There's been little time to cook other things for the meal."

John Jacob stood up so fast that his blond hair flew back from his forehead. "Mama," he said, "let me take the sausages. Maybe I can do something about them."

John Jacob quickly wrapped the sausages in a cloth. Then he hurried out the front door of the shop and into the main street.

He stopped at the blacksmith shop and at the

cartwright shop and at the homes of several farmers. Everyone had enough meat.

Then John Jacob sniffed a strong, rich smell. He sniffed and sniffed until he was right in front of Granny Schmidt's cottage. He peeked over the flower pots on the window ledge. Granny Schmidt was by the oven. She was lifting out fat, round loaves of dark-brown pumpernickel bread. They made John Jacob very hungry.

"Tsk! Tsk!" she muttered, when John Jacob came in the door. "That Hans! He put some of the loaves too near the heat! They are too well done." She made a face at the two pumpernickel loaves. "Which one of our fine customers will buy such loaves as these?"

John Jacob's mouth watered at the sight of the bread. The loaves looked a little lopsided, but he knew they wouldn't taste lopsided.

He opened the cloth to show his sausages. "I'll trade you these sausages for your bread!" he said.

"Ah," said Granny Schmidt. "I haven't had a nice good butcher sausage in a long while."

"These sausages will make a good supper for you along with your bread," said John Jacob.

The old woman's face crinkled with happiness into a thousand wrinkles. She handed John Jacob the loaves of pumpernickel and took the sausages.

When John Jacob arrived back at the butcher shop, everyone was singing. Poppa and Heinrich and George were chopping meat in rhythm to the tune. Mel was taking sausages and bacon and hams out to the smokehouse to be smoked. Even he was singing. John Jacob knew that he wasn't the only member of the family who liked to work hard.

A delicious smell of cooking meat scraps came from across the courtyard.

"Ahhh!" said Poppa, putting down his chopper on the meat block.

"Ahhh!" said Heinrich, patting his stomach.

They all hurried into the house.

Inside the cottage John Jacob climbed into his place at the table by Maria and Catherine. The older boys sat with Poppa at the far end of the long wooden table.

Mama set big wooden plates full of meat before them.

Everyone looked hungrily at the meat. Then John Jacob unwrapped the two loaves of pumpernickel bread.

"You traded the sausages!" Mama said with delight. "What a wonderful trade!"

Poppa Astor looked proudly at his three older sons and said, "I have three big hard-working boys—George and Heinrich and Melchior."

At that, Maria stood up on her stool. "When John Jacob is big, he will be the hardest working of all!" she declared.

"Yes, yes," said Heinrich smiling. "John Jacob is a hard worker."

"Yes, indeed," said Mama, "and he is smart at sausage trading!" She helped herself to a piece of pumpernickel.

"There is no doubting that," said George.

John Jacob was so proud that he could say nothing at all. Besides, with all the meat and pumpernickel he had eaten, he was stuffed as full as a sausage.

A Flute
for School

"THERE'LL BE snowdrifts by morning," said Mama Astor, bolting the cottage door tightly. "Maybe you won't be able to go to school, Jacob." Now that John Jacob was in school, everyone called him Jacob.

"Oh, I must go to school tomorrow," said Jacob. "Tomorrow the schoolmaster is going to teach us how to play the flute. I'm going to be the best flute player in the first class!"

"For shame that you boast so," scolded Mama Astor. She went back to her place by the fire.

Mel laughed, "You always want to be the best, Jacob. You don't even have a flute!"

35

"Oh," said Jacob, pouting. He looked at
George, whittling beside the fireplace. George
was the best flutemaker in Waldorf. "Will you
please make a flute for me, George?" he asked.

"I'll see what I can do," said George, setting down his whittling.

Jacob brought George a long, straight piece of wood from the wood supply. Proudly, Jacob watched his oldest brother trim the wood, bore out the center, and cut the finger holes.

"What good work George does!" said Mama Astor. "I wish he could be apprenticed to a musical-instrument maker, but we have no money to pay an apprentice fee."

"This flute won't be a very good one," said George. "To make a good one, I'd need a lot of time and a better piece of wood."

"Please make it the kind that plays low notes," begged Jacob.

George shook his head and said, "Low flutes are long flutes. Tonight, there's time to make only a short one."

"Now that I'll have a flute," said Jacob to Mel, "I'm going to be the best flutist in my class!"

37

"Ha, ha!" laughed Mel. "Maybe your flute playing won't be any better than your spelling."

Jacob made a face. "Spelling's hard for me," he said. Then his face brightened, and he added, "Arithmetic is easy though! Maybe I'll play the flute as well as I do my arithmetic."

Poppa Astor took his pipe from his mouth and said, "You'll soon be doing all the figuring in the butcher shop. You have a quick mind with numbers, all right."

"There, it's finished at last," said George. He put the flute to his lips and played sweet high notes. "It's the best I can do in a short time."

"Thank you," said Jacob.

"Off to bed with you immediately," said Mama Astor, "or you'll be too sleepy tomorrow to learn anything at school."

Jacob fell asleep dreaming that he was the best flute player in the first class.

In the morning, snow lay in deep drifts. On

his way to school Jacob plunged eagerly through the white snow.

"Do you have your flute?" asked Hans, who was waiting by Granny Schmidt's cottage. Hans waved a long package.

Jacob nodded. The boys hurried toward the old brick schoolhouse next to the church.

Inside, Schoolmaster Valentine Jeune stood before his desk. He was tall and thin and kindly looking. All the students liked him.

Hans and Jacob sat down on the hard wooden bench. Behind them, the older boys were settling into place, Mel among them. Catherine was with the girls in the next room.

Jacob held his flute tightly. He could hardly wait to try it.

First there was spelling. Jacob wrinkled his forehead and tried to remember the words.

At last Schoolmaster Jeune called the first class to the front of the room for flute practice.

The boys stood in a line by the schoolmaster's desk. Each boy played a few notes.

When Jacob's turn came, he put the flute proudly to his mouth and blew.

A thin, shaky tone came out. Some of the older boys laughed. Jacob's face felt hot.

"No! Blow steadily," said Schoolmaster Jeune. "Let's see how Hans does it."

Jacob turned to watch his friend. Hans held up a long, brown flute, with carving down one side. Jacob thought how handsome the flute was. He glanced down at his plain one.

Hans blew, and a dignified, low note sounded.

Jacob blew again. This time he blew hard. A high note and a low note came out together. Neither of them sounded dignified. Jacob could see Mel trying not to laugh.

"No, Jacob," said Schoolmaster Jeune, shaking his head. "How will you ever learn to play Bach?" Then the schoolmaster told the first class to return to the bench and to do the lesson in arithmetic. He then directed the older boys in a folk tune.

Jacob sat and wrote on his slate. Rapidly, he copied down the lesson. The answers popped into his head immediately, and he wrote them down. Hans was still working. His flute was on the bench between them. Jacob stared at it. The flute was exactly the long kind he wanted.

Nudging Hans, Jacob asked, "Where did you get your flute?"

Hans looked up from his slate. "The flute belonged to my great-grandfather," he said. He wrinkled his forehead and returned to his lesson. "Figuring's hard for me," he said.

"I like your flute," whispered Jacob. "Want to trade?" He held up his own flute.

Hans shook his head, and his red hair wobbled on his forehead.

Jacob thought for a moment. "Your flute's an

old one," he said. "It's not new like mine, and it's probably about worn out."

"I still don't want to trade," said Hans. Then he added, "Be quiet! I have to think about these problems. They are very hard."

Jacob couldn't take his eyes off the handsome dark flute. He thought of the dignified tone that had come from it. "If only I had such a flute," he thought. "Then I could be the best player in the first class."

Jacob nudged Hans again and whispered, "Psst! Hans, if you'll trade flutes, I'll do your lesson for you."

"All—right," said Hans, wearily. "I can't do it anyway—not with you always talking to me."

Jacob worked rapidly, copying his answers on Hans's slate. Then the boys exchanged flutes.

Schoolmaster Jeune collected the slates. Then he called the first class up once more for flute practice. The boys lined up before his desk.

Jacob watched Schoolmaster Jeune. The teacher corrected the figuring on the slates, as he listened to individual boys play.

With the handsome flute in his mouth, Jacob stood straight and proud. He filled his fat cheeks with so much air that he felt like a squirrel. He placed his fingers over the holes and blew.

Out came a squeak.

"No, no, Jacob," said Schoolmaster Jeune. Then he stared at the flute. "Isn't that Hans's flute? Well, speak up."

"We traded," said Jacob in a small voice.

"Hmmm," said Schoolmaster Jeune holding up the slate he was correcting. It was Hans's slate. "You traded more than flutes. These answers are not in Hans's handwriting. They are in your handwriting, Jacob."

Jacob hung his head. He wished he hadn't made the trade.

"Hans will never learn his sums if you do them

for him, Jacob," scolded the schoolmaster. "You weren't helping your friend at all. Both of you must stay after school. Jacob will show Hans how to do his sums! The brown flute goes back to Hans! At once!"

The boys exchanged flutes. Then Jacob practiced very hard on the short flute that George had made. Finally a clear note came out.

"You might do almost as well as your brother George," said Schoolmaster Jeune. "Of course, it will take time and hard work."

After school, the two boys sat at the bench working on their slates. Reverend Steiner, the village pastor, came in. Jacob listened to the pastor and the schoolmaster discuss the news of the world. He heard Pastor Steiner talk about the "New Land."

When Schoolmaster Jeune said the boys could leave, Jacob went to the front of the room. He said he was sorry about the trouble he had made.

Schoolmaster Jeune said he could go, but Jacob remained by the desk.

"What is it, Jacob?" asked Schoolmaster Jeune.

"What's the New Land?" asked Jacob.

"Look at this map," said the schoolmaster. He unfolded a large map and spread it out on the desk. He pointed to Germany and to Waldorf, located between Heidelberg and the Black Forest. "See, here's the Rhine River," he said.

Then he followed the Rhine River with his finger. It led into the Atlantic Ocean. He pointed across the ocean to North America. "That's the New Land," he said "That's where many people from Europe are going to live. It's not crowded, the way Europe is."

"Ah, there's talk of war in the New Land, though," said Pastor Steiner. "The colonists want to be free of the English rule."

All the way home through the snow, Jacob and Hans talked of the New Land. At home,

45

Jacob sat on the stoop and traced a map in the snow with a twig.

Mama Astor was feeding her chickens.

"Wouldn't it be fun to go far away?" Jacob asked her.

Mama Astor put her hands on her hips and turned to him. "You should be ashamed of yourself for what you did at school today! Now you can clear a path through the snow. Then the rest of us can get somewhere about the village."

Jacob's Ambition

ONE DAY the following spring, the Astors were singing as they sat around the wooden table in the cottage.

They sang to forget that there was no work to do. They sang, because it was the last time that George would be there to sing with them. He planned to work his way to London.

The hungrier the Astors felt, the louder they sang. They were very hungry, for there had been little butchering business all winter.

If there was no butchering, there was no work. If there was no work, there was no food except Mama's chickens or what Mel raised in

the little garden or what people gave them. They
sang merrily just the same.

When they finished singing, Heinrich helped
George tie up the bundle of clothes he was taking. Jacob sat and watched them.

George took a flute from his belongings and
handed it to Jacob. "This is my favorite," he
said. "You may keep it now."

"Don't you want to take it with you?" asked Jacob as he turned the wooden flute over in his fingers. He looked closely at the holes that George had carved.

George shook his head. "I'll be able to get another flute when I am at Uncle George Peter's in London," he said. "Uncle George has a large factory where he makes flutes and pianos."

Jacob tried to imagine such a factory. "Tell me about it," he begged his brother. Then he listened intently while George talked.

"Many men work at the factory," said George. "They make flutes and pianos with fine tools."

Jacob thought how there were no big factories in Waldorf. The villagers made most of their things at home.

Jacob put the flute to his mouth. It was a handsome long one. He blew into it, but no sound came out. "I will have to blow differently from the way I blow on my old one," he thought.

49

Heinrich was talking. Jacob stopped blowing, and he listened.

"If I were going away," said his fat, jolly brother, "I think that I would go to the New Land in America."

"Right now isn't a good time to go to America," remarked George. "There's talk of war with England. The colonists are up in arms."

Jacob began to play the flute once again. A funny note popped out, surprising everyone. Maria and Baby Lisbet, who was now two years old, giggled. Ann Eve, the brand new baby, smiled in Catherine's arms.

Lately the little girls had been so hungry that they hadn't giggled often. Jacob tried to make the little girls cheerful. He blew more funny notes on his flute.

"Poppa, Heinrich, Mel, and I are all going into the Black Forest with George," said Jacob to the girls. "Maybe the farmers there will have some butchering for us to do after we see George off. Who knows what work we might find!"

Just then, Mel ran in from the butcher shop with a large stick. George tied the ends of the bundle of clothes onto the stick. Mama wrapped up a few pieces of food for George.

Jacob jumped up and took the bundle.

Swinging the stick over his shoulder, he led the family out of the cottage. Poppa joined them with his ox-cart. It was filled with knives and grinders and other butchering tools. All the family walked down the narrow cobblestone street.

Granny Schmidt waved to George from her cottage. Many villagers joined the procession.

Jacob held his head high. For a moment, he forgot that few of the people of Waldorf were as poor as the butcher's family. Jacob looked proudly at George. "Not everyone has an older brother who will learn to make musical instruments in a big factory," he thought.

The villagers followed George to the end of the main street.

At the Roman road, George turned and waved. "Good-bye," he called to the villagers.

"May the Lord bless you on your journey," said Pastor Steiner.

"Work and save your earnings," said Schoolmaster Jeune. "Farewell."

Then George picked up and tossed each one of his little sisters into the air. He promised them he would stay away from the waterspirits and the dwarfs in the Black Forest. He hugged Mama and Catherine.

Poppa started the ox moving, and George took the bundle from Jacob. The brothers set off along the road behind the ox-cart. The trees that bordered the road cast down dark shadows.

After a while, they passed farmers' fields.

"Maybe we can find butchering work to do somewhere along here," said Poppa.

Mel looked out over the fields. He was very much interested in farming. "I don't think so, Poppa," he said. "The farmers around Waldorf have poor soil with which to work. There are too many people living off the soil. None of the farmers here would be rich enough to have butchering done now."

"Waldorf is a jolly place to live in," said Heinrich, "but it isn't a good place in which to make a living. Uncle George Peter was smart to go to London." Then he added, "George is smart to go now, too."

Jacob knew that, first, George was going logging in the Black Forest. He fell into step beside his oldest brother. "How will logging help you get to London?" Jacob asked his brother.

"Logging is just a small business around Waldorf," said George, "but in the Black Forest logging is a large business."

"There are so many ways of making a living!"

thought Jacob. He listened carefully to his brother. He didn't want to miss anything.

"Some person once had an idea about selling logs," George went on, "so he went to many parts of the Black Forest. He found many different people to cut logs for him."

"What about selling them?" asked Jacob. He glanced at the trees along the road. "Who'd want to buy logs, anyway? You can always go out and cut some yourself."

"Not everyone can find trees easily," said George, as he moved his stick of clothes to his other shoulder. "In Holland there's little wood. The people in Holland are happy to have wood to buy from the Black Forest."

Jacob thought about the map in the village school and said, "Holland's way up by the other side of Germany, and the Black Forest's way down here."

George said, "The logs are floated there."

"All the way?" asked Jacob.

George nodded and said, "They're floated down the mountain streams of the Black Forest and then into the Rhine River."

Jacob knew that the Rhine was the main river of Germany. It flowed from the Black Forest up north through Germany and into Holland. Thinking about it, he scratched his head, and said, "Whoever dreamed up so large a logging business certainly must have known a great deal about the world."

"I'm fortunate someone did think it up," said George. "I'm hoping to get to Holland by working with the logs. From there, it will be easy to get across the North Sea to England."

For a long time Jacob was quiet. The wheels of the ox-cart rumbled over the road. Finally George asked Jacob what he was thinking about.

Jacob stuck his thumbs inside his belt. "I'd like to do that when I grow up."

"Do what?" asked Mel, who had been walking on the other side of the ox-cart.

"I'd like to think up a big industry to take things all over the world."

Poppa chuckled up in the ox-cart. "You have big ideas, Jacob!"

Just the same, Jacob kept on thinking about how nice such a future would be.

Loggers

THE ROAD narrowed and wound uphill. The forest became thicker. Here and there the Astors passed sawmills and places where people made wood into charcoal.

"Do you know where we can find the loggers?" Poppa asked a group at a sawmill.

"Go higher into the mountains," the people said. "The loggers are up there."

When the way became steep, Poppa climbed down from the ox-cart. "We won't need butchering equipment up there," he said. "Maybe we'll find some butchering business afterwards, though. We'll collect the cart on the way down."

As Jacob tied the ox to a tree, he heard a rushing sound. He said, "I think there's water close by. Do you hear that?"

"It's a mountain stream," said George.

"Then we ought to find George a job up this mountain," said Poppa Astor. "The loggers use the streams. Follow me."

They followed the mountain stream upward. There was no path, and the Astors pushed their way through the thickness of the forest. The steeper the climb became, the faster the stream rushed down.

"This stream would be good for floating logs," said George.

Jacob looked at his brother with pride. He thought the stream looked far too dangerous for a man to float down it on some logs.

After a while, Poppa stopped. "We should have met some of the loggers before now," he said, puffing from the climb.

"Aren't you too tired to go on, Jacob?" Heinrich asked, puffing too.

Jacob shook his head. He thought about the job that George had to get. It would be terrible if George didn't get to London. Even if George had to start out on a stream like this one, he must not miss his chance in London.

The underbrush along the stream grew dense. "Take off your shoes," ordered Poppa. "We'll wade at the water's edge."

Jacob stepped into the icy water. The stones felt slippery under his feet.

"Be careful!" warned Poppa.

Jacob looked down. The water was rushing over the boulders and swirling into tiny whirlpools. He dropped a leaf into the water. A whirlpool grabbed it and sucked it under.

A roaring sounded ahead, and Poppa urged them all to the bank. "Look out!" he shouted.

A huge wall of water came thundering downstream at them. The spray swished up onto the bank and into their faces.

"It's the logs! They're coming!" shouted George excitedly.

Jacob wiped the spray from his eyes. Behind the big wall of water rushed the logs. They came down the narrow stream in double file. Jacob thought that they looked like long snakes wiggling down the mountain stream. He was surprised at how many there were.

"See how the logs are tied together with willow roots!" said Heinrich. "They come in pairs. Each pair of logs is tied to the pair behind—like a very long narrow raft."

"Look at the men!" shouted Jacob. The men carried long poles and balanced themselves on the rapidly moving logs. They used the poles to push the log raft away from stones and away from the banks. Water flew up in sheets from between the logs onto the men. Their clothes

60

shone from the wetness. The men moved back and forth on the long raft and kept it moving.

From the bank George shouted, "Do you need any help?"

Jacob joined in the shouting. Soon all the Astors were shouting to the men. None of the men glanced up.

The end of the raft wiggled by and out of sight. Jacob listened for the sound of more logs coming downstream. All was quiet.

"Let's go farther up the mountain," said Poppa Astor. He led the way.

The underbrush was not thick now. They walked along the bank.

Soon they heard another noise. After a few minutes, they heard shouting. Then there was a great cracking noise.

The noise stopped, and then the ground seemed to shake. A tree had been cut down, and men were beginning to trim off its branches.

Farther on, they found men working with more logs. Jacob watched them tie the logs together with willow roots.

Poppa Astor walked up to the man in charge. "My son wants to go to England," he told him.

Jacob saw George watching the men.

"I hope they can use me," George whispered with worry in his voice.

The logging boss looked up and said, "Good! Good! We can use another man on the rafts." Then he looked at all the Astor boys. He smiled. "We could use all of your boys to get these logs to the Rhine and on to Holland."

"No," said Poppa, "only one of my sons is going to Holland."

"We're glad to have at least one," said the logging boss. "Come along," he called to George.

Jacob, Heinrich, and Mel crowded around George to say good-bye.

George looked down at Jacob and said, "It's

a good thing you can walk far. I'll send letters home. To pick them up, you might have to go a long distance."

Jacob stood between Heinrich and Mel. He watched George grab a pole and climb onto a narrow log raft.

"You'll have to get used to the work," the logging boss explained.

George eased his feet on the logs, which were wet and slippery. George stuck out his pole and pushed the logs from the bank. The log raft jolted away from beneath him.

Jacob stared. Poppa gasped. George had fallen off the raft!

The logging boss was laughing. George was sitting in the stream. He was wet, but not hurt. All around him the stream pounded downward. It wasn't as dangerous as it looked. The water was only a few feet deep.

"The mountain streams go so fast," the logging boss said, "that they don't seem to have time to dig deep."

George came up on shore, and Heinrich gave him his own dry clothes. George then climbed back on the raft. This time he did not fall off. The family watched him disappear down the mountain stream.

Then Poppa and the three boys climbed down the mountain to their waiting ox-cart.

As they walked, Jacob looked at the trees of the forest. He felt sorry for the people who did not have woods close by. He thought how there must be many valuable things in the forest besides wood.

"Some day," he said to Poppa Astor, "I'm going to bring the things from the forest back to the people who need them."

"Will it be the Black Forest?" asked Mel.

"Are there other forests as rich as the Black Forest?" asked Jacob.

Heinrich plodded along beside him. "School-master Jeune says there are great forests in America."

"You boys!" Poppa said from up in the ox-cart. "We have so little to eat, and you talk about the other side of the world. Be more practical now, Jacob." Poppa pointed to a farmhouse up the road and said, "See that place? Go with Mel and try to get some business."

Jacob hurried along beside his brother. The farmhouse was snuggled into the side of a hill, and the roof was covered with straw. A peasant was sitting on a wooden bench.

"Do you need any butchering done?" asked Jacob. "We have our tools with us."

The peasant took a long-stemmed pipe from his mouth. "No. No. There is no butchering to be done here. We eat very little meat. There's no need for butchering on any of the farms here-about. I'm sorry, son."

66

Jacob kicked his toe at the dirt to hide his disappointment. There was no work here.

A woman came from the house. She wore the highest starched hat that Jacob had ever seen.

"Come in and have some milk!" she said kindly.

Jacob watched her hat as he and Mel followed her. Jacob expected it to totter down onto them. Catherine and Mama had told him of the fancy hats worn by the peasant women of the Black Forest. He looked hard at the hat. He wanted to remember exactly how it looked. It was something to tell them at home, when Poppa, Henrich, Mel, and he arrived with no food.

Inside the house the woman gave Jacob and Mel tall mugs of milk. Jacob drank his milk and set down the mug. As he did so, he heard a noise that startled him.

The woman's face broke into a smile. "That noise was only the cuckoo clock my husband made!" she said.

Jacob turned slowly. The brown clock hung on the wall of the cottage. It was shaped like the front of a little cottage. A wooden cuckoo bird stood outside an open door. When the bird finished calling the time, he swung back, and the door clicked closed. Weights shaped like pine cones swung back and forth beneath the clock.

"It's all done by springs, my lad," said the peasant, coming in the door. Then he pointed to his worktable. There were springs and fine tools all over it.

Poppa sighed when Mel and Jacob came out with no work. "The people are poor around here. Maybe there's work somewhere else," he said.

All the way home, Jacob thought of the different ways there were to make a living. "Why, I probably don't even know about half the ways," he thought.

Jacob Finds
a Job

MARIA FOLLOWED Jacob out of the Astor cottage
one day the next summer.

"Good morning, Jacob!" called Peter Wilhelm,
Jacob's playmate. Peter was standing before
Granny Schmidt's cottage.

Hans Schmidt's face appeared in the cottage
window ledge. "Don't you two have to work?"
asked Hans enviously.

"Poppa has no butchering work," said Jacob
shaking his head.

"Don't be so sad about it," groaned Hans. "I've
been kneading bread dough all morning." He
held up his hands, sticky with globs of dough.

69

Jacob grinned and said, "At least you have plenty to eat!"

"That I have!" said Hans mischievously. He smacked his lips over a glob of dough.

Granny Schmidt's voice came from behind him, "Get back to work, you lazy Hans. You're always into mischief!"

Hans's face turned as red as the red flowers in the window pots. Then he disappeared inside the cottage.

"I should get to work, too," said Peter. "My poppa wants me to help him cut hay. He says we have to get the hay into the barn before it rains. If we don't, some of the hay will rot, and we'd have to dry the rest of it out."

Jacob watched Peter go off to work. Everyone was busy, except the butcher's family, he thought to himself.

"Don't be sad," said Maria. "I'll play with you. Let's go to the mounds."

Jacob looked down at her. "I'm not playing, Maria," he said. "I'm off to look for a job."

"May I have a job, too?" asked Maria.

"No, you're too little," said Jacob, "but you may walk along with me if you like."

"Are you going to find work the way George did?" asked Maria.

"I'm going to find work in the village," said Jacob. "There must be work somewhere."

He went down the cobbled street. Then he turned off onto a lane. At the end of the lane was the cartwright's workshop. Maria climbed onto a sawhorse outside the door and pulled at imaginary reins.

Birch logs were drying against the outside of the workshop. Jacob knew they were for hay wagons. He picked up a small log and stepped into the workshop.

"There's much work to do here," thought Jacob hopefully.

The cartwright was sliding a wheel onto the axle of a new hay wagon.

"The wheel doesn't fit right," said the cartwright. He eased the wheel off the axle. Then he looked up at Jacob.

"I'd like to do some work for you," said Jacob eagerly. "Do you need any help?"

The cartwright took a piece of charcoal from behind his ear. He drew a line on the wood. "Sorry, Jacob. When I want help, I call my sons in—same as your poppa does when he wants help in butchering." His voice softened. "Here in Waldorf, each family works for itself—the way it's always been done."

Jacob went outside and replaced the birch log against the entrance.

Maria jumped off the sawhorse and tugged at his sleeve. "Did you get a job?" she asked.

"I didn't find any work there," said Jacob.

"I'm hungry," said Maria. "I hope you find

73

work." Then she added brightly, "You always think of something, Jacob."

He couldn't think of anything. He felt the bright sunlight on his cheeks. It was a beautiful day for work. He watched the sunshine sparkle on Maria's yellow hair. Up in the sky, the puffy clouds looked like big pink hams.

He heard the clang of a hammer on iron. "Let's go to the blacksmith shop," said Jacob. As they drew near the shop, they could feel the heat from the fire in the forge.

The huge blacksmith was shoeing a horse. Jacob and Maria watched from the doorway. The blacksmith stood by the horse's side. He then held the horse's foreleg up between his own legs, so he could work on the hoof. With the edge of a file, he pried off the old horseshoe. Then he filed down the hoof.

"Ooooh! Doesn't that hurt the horse?" squealed Maria.

74

"No," said Jacob. "The hoof is like a big fingernail. It doesn't hurt you, when you cut your fingernail, does it?"

The horse whinnied, and Jacob went to him. "Gentle, boy, gentle," he said.

The blacksmith grasped some tongs. With them, he pulled a horseshoe from the fire. He pounded the horseshoe into shape and set it on the hoof to see if it would fit.

"It fits," he said in his deep voice. He nailed the shoe on.

Then the blacksmith let go of the horse's leg. He brushed off his big leather apron and straightened up to his full height. "What can I do for you, Jacob Astor?" his deep voice boomed out.

"I want to work for you," said Jacob.

"You want to work for me?"

"I know a lot about horses."

"It's true you can handle horses," said the blacksmith, as he set down his hammer, "but my sons help me when I need any help." Then he picked up the old horseshoe he had removed. He tossed it to Jacob. "Here, take this with you. It might bring you luck."

Jacob thanked the blacksmith. "Luck's not enough," he said. "I've got to do something myself about getting work."

The blacksmith smiled and said, "You're a determined lad, that's for sure."

Jacob and Maria left the blacksmith shop. As they walked on, Jacob rubbed his finger over the worn part of the old horseshoe. He asked others for a job, but no one needed help.

"I have to think where I'm needed," Jacob said to Maria. His arms felt cold. Glancing up, he saw dark clouds over the mountain tops.

"Someone must need help," said Maria.

As the warmth went from the weather, a smile crept over Jacob's face. He thought of Peter cutting hay with his father.

76

"Don't worry, Maria," said Jacob. He put his arm about his sister. "I think I'll find work now."

He hurried so fast over the cobblestones that Maria could hardly keep up.

Maria cried, "You'll never find work now! It looks like rain!"

When they reached the edge of the village, Jacob ran out to the fields. He headed toward the Wilhelm cottage, where Peter's family lived. Maria hurried as fast as she was able.

Jacob stood on the fence by the barn and looked out over the fields.

Peter, his father, and his mother were swinging long scythes through the sweet-smelling hay. Even little Freddie Wilhelm was working. They were all busy cutting hay. "They must not have noticed the weather!" Jacob thought.

He ran to the barn. Quickly, he hitched the horse to the hay wagon. He lifted Maria into the wagon and drove out to the hayfield.

"Get ready to take in the hay," he shouted. "It's going to rain!"

Farmer Wilhelm looked up at the dark clouds. "Those clouds gathered so fast that I didn't notice them at all."

Jacob jumped down and handed out hay rakes. "Up you go," he said to Freddie as he lifted him onto the hay wagon beside Maria.

"If only we can get the hay in before the rain comes!" said Farmer Wilhelm.

Jacob scooped up hay and tossed it onto the wagon. Freddie and Maria laughed with delight as they trampled down hay to make room.

When the wagon was full, Farmer Wilhelm drove the horse to the barn. Hay fell over the sides of the moving wagon like straggly hair.

Jacob held his rake against the packed wagon to keep the hay on.

Thunder crashed off toward the mountains. Bells rang in the village. Jacob knew everyone

78

believed bells would protect the village from lightning. He held his breath, hoping the rain wouldn't start yet.

Just in time Farmer Wilhelm drove the wagon into the barn. Within a few minutes a sheet of rain covered the barn's big doorway. Frau Wilhelm disappeared into the cottage.

The rain was so noisy on the roof that Farmer Wilhelm had to shout. "Jacob, it was a good thing you came," he said. "Some of the hay would have rotted. It would have taken us many days to dry out the rest of it."

Frau Wilhelm came back. "We already have had enough trouble with our crops. The wild boars try to root them up. Thank goodness, the hay wasn't ruined."

She held out a big basket to Jacob. It was filled with grapes and bright red beets and other food. "Take this basket with our thanks, Jacob. We are grateful for your help."

When the storm ended, Jacob and Maria raced home with the basket.

"You found a job after all!" said the hungry Astors when they saw the basket of food.

"Of course, it wasn't a real job—not like George's," said Jacob. He was happy anyway, as he popped a big, juicy grape into his mouth.

A Fright
at School

ONE DAY that fall Jacob and Mel started on their way to school. Heinrich rushed down the street.

"A letter!" he shouted, waving it over his head.

"From George?" asked Jacob.

Heinrich nodded. By now the rest of the Astor family had gathered on the stoop to hear the letter. Mama Astor's few chickens came running up, too, as if they were interested.

Mel nudged Jacob and said, "I'm going on to school. We can hear the letter afterwards."

Jacob shook his head. "There's still time, Mel," he said. "I want to hear if there is any news about the New Land."

"Here's something about it," said Heinrich. "Listen to what George writes:

'All the people in England are talking about the troubles with the American colonies. Most of the ordinary people here sympathize with the colonists. The British want the colonists to buy from British ships and make them pay extra money when they trade goods. This makes the Americans very angry.' "

Jacob clenched his fists at the thought of the injustice to the Americans.

"Here's some more," said Heinrich.

" 'The people of Boston objected to the fines. Then the British Red Coats fired on the colonists and killed some of them.' "

"If the colonists want to do their own trading," Jacob spouted, as he went out the gate, "they should be able to!"

By now Mel had left, and Jacob walked down

the street alone. He paused by Granny Schmidt's cottage. Hans did not come out.

Farther down the main street, Jacob met Hans and Peter. They came in from a side lane which led from the brook.

Hans was grinning broadly, and Peter had a funny look on his face. There was a box in Peter's hands. It was nicely wrapped.

"What's that box for?" asked Jacob.

"We're bringing a present for Schoolmaster Jeune," explained Hans.

"You are?" said Jacob surprised. He looked closely at his friends. It wasn't like Hans and Peter to bring presents to school. It wasn't like them to be anything but mischievous, even though they liked Schoolmaster Jeune.

"Jacob," Hans pleaded, "we need your help."

"What can I do?" asked Jacob.

"Just put this present on Schoolmaster Jeune's desk," said Hans. "That's all you have to do."

"Is that all?" said Jacob. "I'll do that." Then he thought for a moment. Maybe Peter and Hans were up to more tricks. "Why can't you put the present on the desk yourselves?" he asked.

Hans ran his fingers through his red hair. "If —if one of us puts it there, Schoolmaster Jeune might think there was something mischievous about it. Please, Jacob."

"All—right," said Jacob.

Inside the school, Jacob put the present on the schoolmaster's desk. He took his place beside Hans and practiced his spelling.

Schoolmaster Jeune was busy helping a student at the back of the room. He didn't notice the box on his desk.

After a while, the schoolmaster told the boys to stand up and sing. He waved his long arms as they sang a church song.

"Sing louder," the schoolmaster said, smiling. "Sing so loud that you rattle the windows."

The boys began to sing again. Jacob put all his energy into the song. He loved music.

In the middle of the song the door flew open. The boys stopped singing at once.

A red-faced man in a black overcoat stepped into the room. A single eyeglass hung on a ribbon about his neck.

"The school inspector!" Jacob thought. "He came on a surprise visit!"

Inspector Frayley traveled about the countryside. It was his job to see that the village teachers were doing their jobs correctly, and he also checked to see how much the students knew. His report was sent to the district office.

The inspector glanced at Schoolmaster Jeune and shook his head. Jacob knew that Inspector Frayley believed in harsh punishments that Schoolmaster Jeune did not give.

The inspector cleared his throat. "At last it is quiet enough to speak," he said, rapping his cane on the floor. He stood before Schoolmaster Jeune's desk and gave a talk about mischief and the punishments that ought to be given. He took a sharp-edged piece of wood from his satchel. "Disobedient students should have to kneel on this," he said. As he spoke, he pounded his fist on Schoolmaster Jeune's desk.

All the students stood still. Jacob glanced at Hans and Peter. They appeared to be even more scared than the other students. Jacob saw that Hans and Peter were staring at Schoolmaster Jeune's desk.

Jacob glanced at the desk. The present! It was still on the desk. Then Jacob put his hand to his mouth and and stared. The present was moving! There was something alive in it!

Jacob remembered how Hans and Peter had joined him that morning. He thought how they had come in from the path that led to the creek. They must have put a frog in the present box!

Jacob grew hot with anger toward Peter and Hans. If the inspector learned about the frog, Schoolmaster Jeune and the whole school would have to suffer, he thought.

"Let's find out if the Waldorf students know anything," said the inspector. He asked a hard question. Jacob watched the older boys wrinkling their foreheads, searching for an answer.

Then Jacob saw that the present was moving to the edge of the desk. In a moment it would fall onto the floor. The inspector would surely discover the frog!

Before the inspector could see what was happening, Peter broke away from a row of boys and ran to the desk. Jacob saw him rapidly scoop the present over into the wastebasket.

Jacob sighed with relief. Now that the frog was in the wastebasket, the inspector would not notice it.

As Peter came around the other side of the

desk, the inspector grabbed him by the collar. He didn't say anything about the frog.

"Kneel on that wood!" the inspector shouted at Peter. Peter bent down on the inspector's piece of sharp wood. At first, he winced from the pain. Then he bit his lip and looked calm.

Jacob wasn't angry with his friend anymore. "Peter knew he would get punished," he thought, "but he got rid of the frog, anyway."

The inspector turned back to the class. He put his eyeglass to his eye and squeezed his fat forehead down over the rim. He was red with anger.

"You, boy," he turned now to Hans. "Step up here and listen to your question. Quickly! Quickly! I don't have all day!"

Shaking, Hans went to the front of the room. Jacob knew Hans could answer any question about the forest, or about baking, but that he was not very good in his school subjects.

The inspector paused a moment.

"He's thinking up a difficult question," thought Jacob with dismay.

"Ah—let me see," said the inspector. "Now —ah—yes. What was the Boston Massacre?"

"The—the what, sir?" asked Hans.

"The Boston Massacre," the inspector repeated, tapping his cane impatiently.

Hans turned white. He didn't know the answer. He looked as if he thought that the Boston Massacre was some punishment the inspector was going to give him.

The inspector turned to Schoolmaster Jeune. "The Waldorf schoolchildren don't know very much," he said. "I'll have to send in a bad report."

Jacob could see that all the older students were trying hard to think of the answer. The younger children were thinking that now they would lose Schoolmaster Jeune as their teacher.

Then Jacob remembered the letter from

90

George that had come that morning. He remembered what George had written about the colonies. Trembling, Jacob raised his hand.

The school inspector stared at him through his thick eyeglass.

"If you please, Sir. I can answer your question," said Jacob. He told how the British had fired on the American colonists. It was not a question anyone in Waldorf could be expected to answer. Jacob knew how lucky he was that the letter had come that morning.

The inspector opened his mouth in surprise. "That's a smart lad," he said. "I will not have to send in the bad report after all." Swinging his cane, he left the school.

After school was dismissed at the end of the day Schoolmaster Jeune showed Jacob some books about America. They were talking about opportunities in the New Land when Hans and Peter returned to the schoolroom.

"If you please," said Hans to the schoolmaster, "may Peter and I clean the room for you?"

"That would be very nice," said Schoolmaster Jeune. "Very nice, indeed."

Jacob could hardly keep from laughing at the first thing his friends cleaned. They carried the wastebasket outside and emptied it. Then they came back in and cleaned up the schoolroom so well that there wasn't a speck of dirt left anywhere. The room was spotless.

Chasing a Wild Boar

ONE DAY the next spring, Jacob, Peter, and Hans were playing "ship."

"I'll be the captain," said Peter.

"I'll be the pilot," said Hans. "That's almost as good as captain. Then I can steer the ship, at least."

"What'll you be, Jacob?" asked Peter. "All the good posts are taken."

Jacob grinned. "I've thought of a new one," he said. "I'll be the shipowner—then I can say where the ship must go."

"You would think of something like that!" Peter laughed good-naturedly.

What a fine ship the mound made, Jacob thought. It stood on the Waldorf marshland, like a ship standing in water. It was as big and as high as a sailing ship, and the meadow behind it made a good dock.

"Look at the marsh grass," said Jacob. "The wind makes waves through it, just like the waves on the Rhine. Let's pretend we're sailing down the Rhine River."

"All men on deck!" shouted Peter. The three boys stood at the "prow" of the mound and peered out over the waving marsh grass.

"*Whoosh!*"

"What was that?" whispered Hans.

"I think it's something back by the meadow," said Peter. He went to the other end of the mound and motioned the others to follow him.

"Listen to that," he whispered, pointing down to the meadow. Jacob and Hans looked down. The sound came again, faintly.

94

"What is it?" asked Hans, his face so white that his freckles stood out. "A ghost?"

They heard a grunt. The boys looked at one another. They heard another grunt.

"Ghosts don't grunt," said Jacob. "It sounded more like a pig to me."

"Maybe," gasped Peter, "maybe it was a wild boar. Boars grunt."

"I hope not," said Jacob. He had helped farmers chase wild boars. He knew boars were related to pigs. Like pigs on the loose, wild boars gobbled up the crops and dug out growing roots. Jacob shuddered as he thought on. "If you meet a boar, you are in danger of your life!" he had often heard the farmers say.

Now Jacob looked over the meadow—whatever it was, was gone now.

"Listen!" said Peter, pointing off beyond the meadow. "Listen."

There was a faint sound of horns.

Hans brushed his fingers through his red hair. He turned to Peter and Jacob. "Remember that whooshing noise we heard before? I bet it was a ghost! It came to haunt us!"

"What do you mean?" asked Peter.

"Oh, Hans, you're always worrying about ghosts," laughed Jacob.

Hans tossed his head. "Granny Schmidt says that long ago there was an old hunting castle here—maybe a thousand years ago. Granny says that sometimes ghosts of hunters come back."

Jacob laughed. "Ghosts are just something people imagine," he said. "The sounds we heard were probably the horns of real hunters."

"Maybe they're hunters from the castle," said Peter, as he remembered that Schwetzingen Castle was only a few miles from Waldorf.

Jacob nodded. He knew that wealthy gentlemen often visited the castle. Sometimes the visitors went hunting in the countryside.

The sound of the horns grew louder. A pack of tall, graceful greyhounds raced onto the meadow. The boys watched from the mound top.

"They're going toward the marsh!" yelled Hans. "Look at them!"

Yelping excitedly, the dogs dashed to the edge of the marsh grass. One dog stuck his paw into the muck of the marsh and backed away.

"Look at the hunters!" said Jacob, pointing back to the meadow. Five men on horseback rode into view. They wore long, red jackets and held spears across their saddles. The feathers on their three-cornered hats fluttered in the breeze as they rode.

Jacob gulped in wonder at the grace of the horses. Their shiny coats rippled as they leapt over the hedge and toward the mound.

The tall leader of the hunters pulled in his reins and looked up at the boys. "We're chasing a boar," he said. "Have you lads seen him?"

Hans shook his head rapidly.

"Something went across the meadow," Peter said, very politely.

Jacob thought about the strange whooshing sound they had heard. "I think I can help you find the boar, Sir," he said.

Peter gulped and said, "Jacob, we don't know which way it went."

"I think I know," said Jacob. "I bet the boar went into the marsh. After all, wild boars are like pigs, and pigs like to wallow in mud. The marsh is full of mud. I figure that's where the boar went."

"The marsh?" said the leader. "We can't very well go into that mud."

"We could try, Sir," said Jacob. "I know parts of the marsh where it's safe to walk. I've gone in there many times."

"All right," said the leader. "Climb up behind me on the horse, lad. Let's see what you can do."

Jacob eased himself onto the beautiful horse and clutched the hunter's jacket. There was a handsome hunting knife in the man's belt.

Jacob pointed toward the far end of the marsh. "Let's head over there." He waved good-bye to Hans and Peter, who watched from the top of the mound.

The dogs crowded about them. Jacob caught his breath as the horse carried them along into the marsh. After a while, he heard the horse's hoofs making squashy sounds.

"I think we'd better walk from here on, Sir," Jacob said to the leader. "The horses are too heavy for the marsh ground." He slid down from the horse. The hunters dismounted and followed him into a high part of the marsh. Hans and Peter looked as small as black specks back on the mound. He hurried on.

Jacob could feel the ground sinking beneath each step. He moved as rapidly as he could.

He saw no sign of the boar. "Maybe it wasn't such a good idea to come here after all," he thought, looking toward his left. Then—

Off to that side, the marsh grass was matted down. It looked as if an animal had passed through.

Jacob heard a grunt. He listened closely. With a *whoosh*, a wild boar ran out only a few yards before him. It thrashed on.

"He's heading for the mound!" called Jacob. The hunters ran back to their horses, and Jacob followed the boar.

The beast humped up his back and skittered on short legs. He grunted angrily.

Jacob could hear the thundering of the horses' hoofs as they galloped toward the mound.

The boar stopped before the mound. Jacob sped on to the dry land.

The boar pointed his sharp tusks upward at Peter and Hans on the mound.

100

Jacob ran in close. His heart was beating loudly. Jacob feared for the safety of his friends.

The boar turned. The greyhounds passed Jacob and surrounded the boar. The animal lowered his two ugly tusks at them.

"He'll rip the dogs apart with those tusks," said the leader. He whistled, and the dogs came away from the boar.

Jacob gulped. Now there was nothing between himself and the boar.

The boar's ears wobbled, and the bristles on his back stood up. "He's really mad!" thought Jacob with dismay.

The boar reared about and raced straight toward Jacob. Shuddering, Jacob turned.

A spear flew from the hand of one hunter. It hit the boar's thick hide and bounced off. The boar grunted hoarsely. Then he came on, straight at Jacob with his tusks lowered.

Jacob stumbled and fell!

With a spear in his hand, the leader ran close to the beast and stuck it behind the ear.

Slowly, the boar fell to the ground. His eyes flashed. He started to rise. Then he fell back and lay still.

Hans and Peter ran down to Jacob.

"We can have roast boar for our feast when the prince visits the castle tomorrow!" one of the hunters said. The hunters all cheered.

The leader looked at Jacob. "Thanks to the help of this Waldorf lad, we found the boar," he said. "Our hunt was a success!"

Jacob was thinking about the feast. He looked at the boar. "Wild boars," he thought, "are like the pigs that Poppa makes into hams and bacon, when there is business." He turned to the leader. "If you're having a feast, Sir," he said, "you'll need a good butcher to prepare the boar."

The leader appeared pleased and said, "Why, yes! We will need a butcher."

"My father is a very good butcher," said Jacob. "I know our family could prepare the boar."

The leader accepted Jacob's suggestion.

Proudly, Jacob led the hunting party into the village of Waldorf.

Poppa took out his butchering tools. "One thing," he said to the family, "Jacob knows how to get business."

Soon Heinrich, Mel, and Poppa were busy butchering the boar. Even Catherine and Mama left their mending and spinning to help.

Before he left, the hunting leader said, "Tomorrow we are having a feast in honor of the visiting prince. I'm inviting all of Waldorf to the castle to see the fireworks."

Fireworks at the Castle

Jacob sat on the stoop and polished the buckles on his shoes. Humming, he glanced at the rest of the family in the courtyard. He wore an old Sunday coat. It had been worn by George, then Heinrich, and then Mel. Now it was Jacob's best coat for special occasions.

Maria and Lisbet stood on tiptoe by Mama Astor. Long, colored ribbons hung down from Mama's best cap.

"What pretty ribbons, Mama," said Maria. Little Lisbet tried to touch the ribbons. "No, no, Lisbet," said Maria, who was six now. She finished braiding Lisbet's hair into a fat pigtail.

Heinrich was trying to button his best black frock coat. His stomach was so big, the button-holes would not reach the buttons. Heinrich laughed about it till tears ran down his cheeks.

In one corner, fifteen-year-old Catherine was smiling up at her suitor. George Ehninger was the son of a tradesman in Waldorf, and he wanted to marry Catherine. Singing a gay song, George Ehninger grabbed Catherine's hands. He swung her into the middle of the courtyard. Her bright-colored skirt whirled out.

Setting down his shoe rag, Jacob played a merry dance tune on his flute. Lisbet and Maria beat time with their feet.

Even Mama and Poppa began to dance.

Everyone was laughing in the courtyard when Mel came in.

"Don't waste all your strength," called Mel. They all stopped. "You'd better save some for the long walk to the castle."

Poppa sighed. He let go of Mama's arm. "Yes, yes. Of course," he said, "Mel is right."

"Everyone's starting now," said Mel, dusting off the sleeves of his black frock coat. Then he looked at Maria and Lisbet. "The little girls aren't coming along, I hope."

"Of course they are," said Jacob.

"But it's so far to the castle, and they're too young." Lisbet and Maria looked as if they were going to cry.

"They had better stay with Granny Schmidt, along with baby Ann Eve," said Mel.

"Perhaps they shouldn't go," said Poppa.

"Please let them," begged Jacob. He couldn't bear that they should be unhappy. "I'll help them get there."

"They will be your responsibility then," said Poppa. "You must take care of them."

Jacob and his family joined the procession of villagers. Peter brought his little brother Freddie, and others brought younger sisters and brothers with them.

"I'll try to help you," Hans said to Jacob. Hans was trying to flatten down his hair so he would look neat at the castle. Each time he ran his hand over his head, his red hair sprang back up. He held Maria's hand, while Jacob walked with Lisbet.

The procession passed a wandering student from Heidelberg and a farmer with a cart.

A stagecoach came by, and the villagers stood at the side of the road to let it pass.

Jacob gazed at the horses. All the women marveled at the beautiful clothes of the ladies inside.

"Some day I'm going to be rich and have fine horses," said Jacob.

"Imagine!" laughed Hans. "A butcher of Waldorf with such fine horses!"

In the afternoon the villagers rested beside the road. When the procession was about to start once more, Lisbet clung to Jacob's coat. "I'm tired," she complained.

"Don't you want to stay awake for the fireworks?" asked Jacob.

Lisbet didn't answer. Her mouth was stretched wide in a yawn.

"Can't you do something about those girls," called Poppa to Jacob.

"Maybe I shouldn't have brought them," thought Jacob with disappointment. "If only I had a horse or a coach." He made up his mind to do something.

He gathered some sticks about the resting place. Then he handed them to all the little girls and boys. "Let's pretend we're soldiers of Frederick the Great. These sticks will be our rifles," he said. "Put the rifles over your shoulders and march ahead!" Jacob played a tune on his flute.

In a moment the children were marching briskly down the road. They marched to the head of the procession. Peter, Hans, and Jacob hurried to keep up with them.

When darkness fell, the Waldorf villagers stepped through the gates of the castle grounds.

Jacob looked about in awe. Light from paper lanterns sparkled on marble statues. Two reindeer fountains sent water high into the air, and more water splashed down marble steps.

"Ummm. I smell lilacs!" said Maria.

Jacob sniffed the sweet scent. The purple blooms were everywhere.

"Look at the castle!" said Lisbet, her eyes wide open now. "How beautiful!"

Lights twinkled from the windows. Ladies in powdered wigs and beautiful silk gowns stepped out onto the balconies.

"Oooh! The ladies look like fairies!" said Lisbet. "I'm glad you brought us, Jacob."

Jacob saw tables inside the castle. They were laden with food.

"The cake has hundreds of layers!" said Maria.

"Some day I'll have enough money so I can have all the food in the world," said Jacob.

"Oh, Jacob!" laughed Maria. "You have such big ideas!"

Then Schoolmaster Jeune pointed to a balcony. The visiting prince came out, and the villagers cheered.

The lord who had led the hunting party came down from the castle. "I'll take you to the fireworks grounds," he said to the villagers. To Jacob he looked even taller than he had the day before.

"I wish I were as tall as he!" said Peter.

"I'm even shorter than you are," said Jacob, to his friend. He tried to stretch as tall as he could. He still wasn't very tall.

Jacob took Maria and Lisbet by the hand and hurried them along. "Wait till we see the fireworks!" he said, happy he had brought the girls.

The lord directed them all to a long field. At

one end was a hill. "The rocket machinery's up there," the lord said, pointing to the hill.

Jacob looked all about. He noticed a large wooden framework. He went close up to see it. The framework was made in the shape of a Greek temple, with boards for pillars.

"You better stay back from that framework, lad," called the lord.

"How does it work?" Jacob asked him.

"When it's lit, it will blaze in the shape of a temple," explained the lord.

"We can't see! We can't see!" All the small children were complaining. Jacob saw that the fine gentlemen and ladies from the castle had gathered in front of them.

"Where may I put the children?" Jacob asked the lord. "They can't see."

The tall lord looked down at the children. "Follow me," he said. "You children will have a good place to sit." He led them around in front

112

of all the grand folk. The children sat on the ground in front of everyone else. They had a good view of the temple framework.

Two soldiers were in charge of the fireworks. For the first display, they stuffed straw into a large wheel of oak wood. They set the straw on fire and pushed the wheel over the hillside. The flaming wheel rolled faster and faster. Then it turned on its side and slowly slid down the hill. The wheel banged against the far side of the framework and made it tremble.

The wheel rolled away and stopped. Jacob and Peter and Hans ran after it. They tore off the smoldering straw and rolled the wheel back to the lord.

Jacob returned to the children. A rocket whizzed from the hill up into the sky. It burst into a star, and the points went sizzling off in all directions.

Four more rockets went up.

Then a voice came from the hill, "Quiet, please. We are about to light up the temple. Quiet, everyone."

Jacob watched a soldier run down the hillside holding a burning torch. The soldier put the torch to one end of the framework.

"We have the best view of all," squealed Maria happily. "It's wonderful!"

The temple began to burn, and the flame dashed like a snake across the framework. The crowd settled back peacefully to enjoy the sight.

"It's like fairyland," whispered Lisbet.

Jacob saw her stand up. "Stay back!" he warned. He grabbed her and made her sit down.

Then another rocket whizzed from the hill. It zoomed straight upwards. Everyone watched it explode into bright red stars.

Jacob heard a noise close by. He glanced at the temple. As he looked, a flaming pillar loosened itself from the framework. It tottered a few seconds and crashed down. Horrified, Jacob watched it. Then he jumped up.

"Sit still!" he called calmly to the children, but they began screaming and running about.

"If they don't get burned, they'll be crushed," Jacob thought. He looked for Hans and Peter, but they, too, were running about with fright. He knew he had to do something.

Then he cupped his hands over his mouth and called. He made his voice loud and calm. "All of you. Keep quiet," he called. "Keep calm!"

He grabbed Peter and Hans. "Help me get the children into a line," he said.

In a few moments the children were marching out of danger. The flames of the temple went out.

The villagers watched the rest of the rockets from the far end of the field.

As the villagers left, the lord handed out baskets of food. "Here's cake for you to munch on, walking home," he said.

Jacob saw the lord stop Poppa and talk with him. Jacob heard the lord say, "Your Jacob is a fine lad. He helped us in our hunt, and he organized the children very well during the fire.

Something great will come of that son of yours some day. You will see."

Jacob couldn't keep a smile from his face. He felt tall and important.

Then he heard his father's answer: "Don't put ideas into the boy's head. His future is as a butcher in Waldorf."

"I won't be a butcher in Waldorf when I grow up," Jacob thought, but he wondered how he could be anything else.

A Strange Trade

Jacob poked his head from under the striped awning of the booth. "Chicken! Nice roasted chicken for sale!" he called.

Booths lined the market square in front of the church. It was the harvest fair of 1774. The Astors had no sausage or ham to sell, so they were selling Mama Astor's chickens.

"Buy it here!" eleven-year-old Jacob shouted.

"Grapes!" "Cuckoo clocks!" "Nice fresh bread!" shouted the other tradesmen.

Poppa Astor mopped his brow with a big, red handkerchief. "Nobody wants hot chicken in this warm weather," he said. "It's such a hot fall!"

Mama Astor sighed, as she turned more chicken on the spit. "How will we get through the winter with no money?" she said.

"I know what!" said Jacob. "I'll take a basket of chicken and peddle it in the crowd."

"They can come here to buy chicken if they want any," said Poppa. "It's too hot to go about."

"I'll make people buy some," said Jacob, wrapping chicken pieces in a clean cloth. He put the chicken in a wicker basket and swung the basket onto his shoulder.

He edged his way through the crowded square. "Chicken for sale!" he called loudly.

A farmer from the countryside bought some, and a woman from the next village bought some more, but no one else seemed hungry.

He saw Peter and Hans working at their family stalls. Customers clustered about the other stalls. "If only I could get a crowd in front of our stall!" Jacob thought to himself.

He followed the sound of fiddles. He set down his basket by a group of dancers. Then he took out his old flute and played along with the fiddling. The dancers whirled about.

"Nice roasted chicken to eat!" he called when the dance was ended.

"It's too hot to eat," the dancers replied.

Jacob walked to the edge of the village. Sadly, he thought how little he had sold. He sat down at the edge of the Roman road. He wiped his forehead with the bottom of his smock. "How will we ever get through the winter?" he thought.

Two young men were coming down the road. They walked slowly and carried heavy knapsacks on their backs. Jacob knew they must be students from Heidelberg. He wondered what they were carrying in the knapsacks.

The students slipped the knapsacks off their backs and flopped down, exhausted.

One student, a lanky young man, looked at

Jacob and said, "Is that a fair going on in the village over there?"

Jacob nodded.

"I suppose they sell food?" asked the other student who was plump. "We're hungry."

"Yes, indeed!" said Jacob as he jumped up. "I have tasty roasted chicken for sale right here." He took his basket to them and lifted the cloth.

The chicken looked dry by now, he thought. Anxiously, he glanced at the students.

The plump student was rubbing his stomach. Even the lanky student was licking his lips.

"Looks good," said the plump student.

Jacob smiled broadly.

Then the lanky student shook his head. "That chicken won't do us any good," he said. "We can't buy it. We have no money."

Jacob's heart sank. At last he had found hungry customers, but they couldn't pay. Then he looked at the knapsacks. If he couldn't get money, he thought, maybe something else would work. Jacob pointed to the knapsacks.

"Do you have anything in those knapsacks to trade for the chicken?" asked Jacob.

"Ahhh," said the lanky student. "I'd almost forgotten. Our knapsacks contain magic from America." Jacob watched eagerly as the student unfastened the leather straps of his knapsack.

"Look at the magic," said the student, holding the knapsack open.

Jacob peered in. He saw lumps, the size of apples. They were dark and smelled of dirt. He stood up. Planting his short legs firmly on the ground, he eyed the students. "Your magic does not look like much," he said.

The plump student's mouth curled into a smile, and his smile became a laugh. He shook all over. Finally he stopped laughing. "No, these potatoes don't look like much," he said, "but they're valuable if you have a little land for planting them."

122

"What do you mean?" asked Jacob.

"Well," explained the lanky student, "all over Europe the peasants are begininng to grow this crop. They're called 'potatoes.' "

Jacob laughed, "Po—ta—toes? That's a funny name for a food!"

"It's an Indian name," said the lanky student.

"Potatoes are the safest crop you can grow," said the plump student. "Nothing'll ruin the crop. You can grow a supply on one small plot of land that will last for months."

"So much food from one small plot?" Jacob thought how it would be food for the winter.

"You should boil the potatoes and mash them," said the plump student, looking hungrier as he spoke. "Then put butter on them. They're delicious. Everyone in America is eating them."

Jacob thought how the villagers would laugh if he let himself be cheated.

He put his fists to his waist and looked the students straight in the eye. "Are you telling me the truth about these?"

"Yes," said the students, looking back without flinching. "It's the truth."

"All right. Let's trade," said Jacob, convinced now that they were honest.

"We'll trade you a dozen potatoes for the chicken," said the lanky student.

Jacob shrugged. "No," he said.

"You won't trade?" asked the plump student.

Jacob shook his head. "What good would a dozen potatoes do?" he asked. "If they're as valuable as you say, I'll need more than a dozen—" He cleared his throat and said. "I'll need all of the potatoes in your knapsacks."

"There's not much chicken," said the lanky student looking at the basket.

Jacob thought a while. He knew the students were tired of lugging the potatoes. If he could offer them something along with the chicken,

124

maybe they would trade all the potatoes. He reached into the pocket of his smock and pulled out his old flute. "I'll give you this along with the chicken," he said.

"Here, let me try it out," said the plump student. He played a Mozart melody, and his companion brightened at the pleasing sounds. "That'll make our journey pleasant."

The lanky student held out his hand to Jacob. "It's a trade." They shook hands.

Jacob gave him the chicken. Then he pulled off his smock and spread it on the ground. The potatoes tumbled from the knapsacks onto the smock. Then the students went off chewing drumsticks.

Jacob gathered up the edges of the smock and swung the potato load over his shoulder. The handle of the wicker basket hung over his arm. The basket bounced at his side as he walked toward the square, whistling.

As Jacob neared the square, Hans and Peter came running from their family stalls.

"What do you have there, Jacob?" called Hans.

"I've made a bargain!" Jacob called back. "Come and see what I have."

Other fair-goers looked curiously at Jacob. A group followed him to the chicken booth.

Beneath the striped awning, Jacob lowered his smock to the ground. He stood up and brushed the hair from his eyes. Everyone was looking at him.

"Let's see what you have there," said Heinrich. He peered at Jacob's bundle.

Poppa Astor wiped his hands on his red handkerchief. With his hands on his hips, he stood waiting to see. Mama and Mel joined them. Catherine, who was married now to George Ehninger, came and looked, too.

Jacob untied the smock. Peter held up a potato. The people crowded to see.

126

"Looks as though Jacob's been cheated," said Granny Schmidt. "It's just a lump of dirt."

"Just a root," laughed someone else.

"Like food for pigs and boars," laughed another fair-goer.

Jacob felt his face reddening. He swallowed hard. "No," he said. He talked so quietly the crowd had to stop laughing. "Potatoes don't look like much, but they make a good crop. Besides, they're good-tasting."

"Good-tasting?" asked Hans. Before Jacob could stop him, Hans grabbed a potato. With a laugh, Hans bit off a chunk and chewed noisily. Then Hans jumped back. "It tastes bad!"

Jacob started to laugh, and soon the crowd was roaring. Finally Jacob wiped the tears of laughter from his eyes. "Oh, Hans," he said, "you can't eat potatoes raw. They have to be cooked and mashed."

"Show us," said Granny Schmidt.

Jacob set a kettle of water on the fire to boil. As the crowd watched, Jacob peeled five potatoes. When the water began to boil, he dropped the potatoes into the kettle.

While the people waited to see what would happen to the potatoes, they became hungry.

"I'll buy some of that chicken," said a man. "Waiting makes me hungry."

Two more people bought chicken, and Poppa and Mama hurried about, serving it.

When the potatoes were cooked, Jacob mashed them with a wooden spoon. He sprinkled salt on them, and added yellow lumps of butter. Steam rose from the mixture.

"Smells mighty good," said Granny Schmidt, but how does it taste?"

"Here, Granny," said Jacob, "you taste some and see." He held the spoon out to her.

Granny took a tiny bite. Then her face wrinkled up with pleasure, and she finished the spoonful. "It's delicious," she said. She saw a man eating chicken. "I think these potatoes would go nicely with some of that chicken."

"I'll have chicken with potatoes, too," said another woman from the village.

Soon all the crowd was eating potatoes and chicken. More fair-goers gathered.

"Let's keep some of the potatoes for planting," said Jacob. "Don't you think so, Mel?"

"Yes, indeed," said Mel, looking the potatoes over. He was always interested in farming. "I heard somewhere that people were growing these in Germany, but I didn't give it too much thought. Now I believe the wonderful things I've heard about them."

"Jacob has vision," said Heinrich. "Jacob can see a good opportunity. I would never have traded for the potatoes, but he saw that it was a good trade item."

"He'll make a fine butcher," said Poppa.

Jacob, however, was thinking that being a butcher in Waldorf wasn't a good opportunity at all. He had to tell Poppa.

"Poppa—" he began. So many people were ordering chicken now, that Poppa didn't hear. "It's not a good opportunity at all to tell him how I feel about being a butcher." Jacob thought, hurrying to help with the orders.

Danger in the Smokehouse

ONE BUSY morning during the harvest season of 1775, the Astor's meat grinder broke.

Jacob, who was twelve years old now, and Mel carried it out to the ox-cart.

"I wish Heinrich hadn't gone to America," said Mel. "He knew all about preparing the meat. We wouldn't be having so much trouble now."

"Farmer Beekman is the only villager who wants butchering done though," said Jacob. "There's no more business after his work is done."

"There might be some, if we do a decent job with Farmer Beekman's meat," said Mel. "It's our only chance for more business."

"There's plenty of business in America," said Jacob. "That's what Heinrich writes."

Now letters came from Heinrich in America, as well as from George in London. The letters made Jacob want to leave Waldorf.

"All ready, sons?" said Herr Astor as he hurried out the courtyard gate. He brushed off the sleeves of his best black waistcoat. It was patched and mended, and the lace at the wrists was old.

Mama Astor and the little girls hurried behind Poppa Astor, calling "Farewell."

Jacob glanced at the ox and ox-cart. "Poppa," he said, "may I go to Heidelberg with you?"

Poppa Astor took his pipe from his mouth and said, "Jacob, it's no good always wanting to go places. I think you'd learn a lesson from Heinrich. Look what happened to him! He went over to the British colonies in America. Now there's a war going on around him."

"When the colonists win the war though," said Jacob, "England will no longer rule them. America will become a free country, and everyone will have a chance to make something of his life. I think Heinrich is glad he went." He handed the meat grinder to his father.

"We need your help here," said Poppa Astor. "Mel can take care of the farming for us, and Heinrich showed you some of the matters about butchering."

Mama Astor held up Ann Eve to kiss Poppa Astor good-bye. Then Poppa Astor waved to everyone and set off down the road to Heidelberg. It was a beautiful day.

Jacob bit his lip as he watched his father go. For once, he was too restless to want to work, but the meat had to be prepared. He turned back to the butcher shop.

Jacob took Heinrich's old place behind the chopping block. He took a long knife and

134

trimmed fat from a big, pink ham. He smelled the spices Mama Astor was mixing into the sausage meat. At the bench by the door, eight-year-old Maria was showing Lisbet how to stuff sausages. Lisbet watched carefully.

"You mustn't get them lumpy and bumpy," Maria warned Lisbet.

Jacob remembered how he had stuffed sausages once and smiled.

Ann Eve poking her head in the doorway said, "Mel's in the smokehouse. He says to hurry. He wants to start smoking the meat right away."

Mel appeared suddenly behind her. "There's no sawdust!" he exclaimed "We can't make smoke without sawdust!"

"I'll go up to the sawmill and see if there's any sawdust there," Jacob offered, setting down the knife on the chopping block.

"I'll help you carry it back," said Maria.

Jacob grabbed up two hams like babies in

arms and Maria carried the sausages. They followed Mel out to the smokehouse.

The smokehouse was a small wooden building. Jacob stepped onto the dirt floor.

"Why aren't there any windows?" asked Maria, who hadn't helped at all with the smoking when Heinrich was still home.

Jacob blinked to get used to the darkness. "We don't need any windows," he said. "The smoke would escape, once the smoking starts. We just close the door and let the smoke cure the meat." He hung the hams onto the hooks on the wall. Maria looped the string of sausages over another hook.

Then Jacob wheeled the pushcart out onto the road, and Maria followed with a yoke of buckets over her shoulder. The empty buckets jerked this way and that on the ropes.

As they walked along to the sawmill, Jacob thought about America. Now that Heinrich was

136

gone, Poppa took it for granted he would stay and be a butcher. "I don't want to stay in Waldorf forever and ever," Jacob thought.

He wheeled the pushcart up to the sawmill. Maria followed him to the big saw and knelt down beside the piles of sawdust. "There's plenty of it," she said happily. Then she started to sneeze. "Ah-choo!"

"Ah-choo!" Jacob sneezed, too. "It's mighty dusty in here." He turned away.

He felt Maria set something scratchy over his ears. She stood back and laughed, "You have such beautiful long curls, Jacob!"

He pulled the planed-wood curls from his ears and grinned.

Maria clapped her hands. "At last I've made you smile!" she said happily. "All day you've been looking so sad. What's the matter?"

"Oh, Maria—" Jacob blurted out. "I want to go to America!"

"Why can't you?" asked Maria.

Jacob looked downcast, and said, "How would I ever get Poppa to let me go?"

Maria put her head in her hands and thought a moment. Finally, she tossed back her braid. "You must tell Poppa when he comes home from Heidelberg, Jacob," she said as she stamped her foot. "You must let him know that you want to go to America."

Together, they scooped the sawdust into the buckets and the pushcart. Jacob felt better now, as they hurried back.

The smokehouse was all ready, with a layer of straw on the floor.

"Do you think that's enough?" asked Mel.

"It looks right to me," answered Jacob. "Heinrich didn't tell me much about this."

"I don't know much about it either," said Mel. "It's been a long time since we've had any customers who wanted meat smoked and cured."

138

"We'll have to make the best of it," said Jacob. Mel helped him spread sawdust over the straw. Then they sprinkled water over the sawdust.

"Do you think that's enough water?" asked Jacob. "I could get more from the rain barrel."

Mel shrugged his shoulders and said, "I don't remember, but I guess so."

Jacob and Maria watched from the doorway as Mel held a flame to the straw.

"What happens now?" asked Maria.

"Pretty soon the smoke will start rising," Jacob explained. "The sawdust makes the smoke and the smoke rises into the meat. Smoking keeps the meat from spoiling and also gives it a nice flavor."

Jacob kept his eye on Mel. He stood ready to close the door as soon as Mel came out. He knew the smokehouse should be airtight.

Just before he closed the door after Mel, Jacob glanced at the smokehouse floor. A yellow flame leapt up through the sawdust. Jacob shivered.

"There's not supposed to be any flame," he said. "There's just supposed to be smoke!"

"Fire!" shouted Maria.

Mama Astor came running from the butcher shop. She threw up her hands. "The Beekman's meat will be ruined!" she cried. "No one else will give us work!"

Jacob grabbed some buckets. He ran to the rainbarrel and scooped out water. He hurried back and poured water onto the sawdust. The flames died down, and soon the wet sawdust was smoldering properly, sending deep fumes of smoke into the meat.

Mama Astor gazed at the meat with relief. "Thank goodness for Jacob. None of the Beekman's meat has been burned."

When the ox-cart clattered down the street from Heidelberg that afternoon, the Astor family rushed out to greet Poppa.

"The grinder's fixed," said Poppa Astor. "It'll

work fine." He smiled down at the family from his seat in the ox-cart.

Before he could say anything more, Mel told him about the fire. "Jacob saved the meat for us," said Mel.

Poppa Astor climbed down from the ox-cart. He put his hand on Jacob's shoulder and said, "You did a fine job, son. You have your wits about you. I'm glad I have you to take over the butcher business."

Jacob swallowed hard. He felt trapped. "But, Poppa—" he began.

Before Jacob could say more, Poppa Astor took a piece of paper from his pocket. "Here's a letter from George. He's written something special for Mel:

'There is a place in Uncle George Peter's flute and piano business for another person —Mel, why don't you come to London and work with us.'"

"Me?" asked Mel, his eyebrows raised in surprise. "George wants me to come?"

"You've never liked butchering, Mel," said Poppa Astor. "Maybe this is the chance for you, after all. Would you like to go to London?"

"You're lucky, Mel," said Jacob, excited for his brother. "What a wonderful chance!"

"I don't want to go to London," said Mel, "or to any city. I want to stay in Germany and be a farmer."

Maria put her hands on Jacob's arm. "Tell Poppa now," she whispered.

"Poppa," Jacob cleared his throat. "Poppa, I don't want to be a butcher either. Maybe— couldn't I go to London in Mel's place?"

Mama Astor threw up her hands and exclaimed, "You go to London, child? You're much too young!"

Poppa Astor looked at Jacob sternly. "It wasn't you George sent for, Jacob," he said.

"I want to be a trader, Poppa," pleaded Jacob.

"Butchering is a good enough trade," said Poppa Astor, "and we need you here." His voice was harsh, and Jacob knew there was no arguing.

Downcast, Jacob unhitched the ox and led it away to the shed.

He heard Maria running up. "Jacob," she said when she was beside him, "don't worry. You'll get away somehow. I know you'll get to America, and you'll do even better than George." She added, smiling, "I'm sure of it!"

Raftsmen on
the Rhine

THE NEXT spring Jacob was hiking with Hans and Peter. Ahead of them stretched the smooth paving of the Roman road. It led straight toward the Rhine.

Jacob reached inside his pocket. His fingers touched the folded letter he had written.

"I hope we can find a raftsman to take your letter to George," said Peter.

Jacob glanced ahead, looking for the Rhine. They had been walking since morning. He saw only acres of grapevines and birds flitting about.

"Here, Jacob, catch," said Hans, as he tossed a biscuit. He took another from his pocket.

Jacob caught the biscuit and bit into it. "Umm. Thanks," he said. He wished he didn't have to depend on his friends for food. There was less food than ever at the Astor home, even though there was one less person to eat it. Mel had become a tenant farmer at Neuwied in another part of Germany.

Peter dug a biscuit out of his own pocket, and the boys walked along munching on their snacks.

"Next year is our last year of school," said Jacob. "Our school days will soon be over."

"I'm going to be apprenticed to the cartwright," said Peter. "I can hardly wait!"

"I'm going to be a baker," said Hans proudly. "That's what I've always wanted."

Jacob swallowed. "I'm not going to be a butcher," he said.

"What about your father?" asked Peter. "He wants you to be a butcher."

"That's why I wrote this letter," said Jacob.

146

"Remember when George wrote and asked Mel to come to England? Now I want George to send for me. I want him to ask me to come when I'm through with school. Maybe then, Poppa will let me go."

"There's not enough butchering work in Waldorf even for your father," said Peter. "There wouldn't be enough if you became a second butcher in the village."

"Anyway," said Jacob, "if I went somewhere else, I could send my earnings back. There's no opportunity for me in Waldorf."

"Look!" shouted Hans. "There's the Rhine!"

Jacob stared at the river ahead. A horse on the opposite bank was towing an excursion boat.

"Look at the sailboats trying to keep their balance!" shouted Peter.

"Look at the houseboats!" shouted Hans.

"There's everything, except a lumber raft," said Jacob with disappointment.

"All that water makes me thirsty," said Hans.

"Let's go find some water to drink," said Jacob. "There are plenty of brooks around here."

Jacob found a brook that tumbled down over a flat rock. He flung himself onto the ground and held his mouth to the tiny waterfall.

"Don't drink it all," joked Hans, getting down beside him on the ground.

"It's the best water I ever tasted," said Jacob, standing up. He took out his flute and played a folk song about the Rhine. Hans and Peter whistled along to the tune, as they walked to the river. Suddenly Jacob took the flute from his mouth and stared up the river.

"A lumber raft!" he shouted. A very wide raft, came down the river. The logs were tied several layers deep. Behind the large raft other rafts were attached.

"Look at all the men!" shouted Jacob, running up to the bank. He waved his arms.

148

"Helloooo! Stop!" yelled Jacob.

One raftsman looked up and waved, but the raft continued down the river.

"It's moving into the bank now," said Hans.

When the three boys arrived near the raft, they stopped and watched it pull into the bank. The raftsmen climbed over onto the land.

"What the matter with the men?" asked Peter. Some of the men were falling down on the land. Others walked about, bent over. Some seemed to be limping.

One red-bearded raftsman laughed at his comrades, "Ha Ha! Ha!"

"Stop laughing, Frederick," the others called. "We'll get our land legs back."

"All that's the matter with them is that they're stiff from being on the river," said Jacob to his friends. Soon the three boys were laughing too. The raftsman Frederick glanced at the boys and roared and slapped his knees.

Then Frederick flopped down on the ground. "Feels good to be on land," he said to the boys, "but it feels even better to be lying down on it."

The boys sat down. Their legs were tired, also.

"We've brought those logs all the way from the Black Forest," explained Frederick.

"I know," said Jacob. "My oldest brother went to London on a raft from the Black Forest."

Then Jacob took the letter from his pocket. "This letter has to go to him in London, Sir. I'd be mighty grateful if you'd take it for me and see that it gets on its way."

Frederick shook his head, and his beard wobbled back and forth.

"You won't?" asked Jacob, with a sinking feeling inside him.

"No," said Frederick. "You can see yourselves how we travel on a raft. No man has enough space for his own things."

"Maybe one of the others——" began Peter.

"You won't find anyone else here to take it," said Frederick. He pointed to a log house built on one of the rafts. "Even the cook has hardly enough space for our food and kettles. I've had to refuse many letters."

"What are you going to do now?" whispered Hans.

Jacob rubbed his finger on the ground as he thought. He had to get his letter to George. If he paid the men, they might take the extra item, but he didn't have any money.

"Would you like to hear some music?" he asked the raftsmen, taking out his flute.

The raftsmen nodded, and he played a folk tune. They began wiggling their feet. Even the cook, who was making stew in a kettle, shuffled his feet around the fire.

"If we weren't so worn out, we'd get up and dance," said Frederick.

"It's mighty good to hear music, after working all day on the raft," said a man next to Frederick. "It's very restful."

"Have some stew with us," said the cook by the fire. He ladled out steaming bowls of stew and handed them around.

Everyone relaxed. As they ate, the men began telling stories.

"We have to get the rafts past the Lorelei," said Frederick, smiling. He pointed down the river. "The Lorelei is a beautiful maiden. She sits on a rock along the Rhine and combs her long, golden hair. She sings an enchanting song. Whoever hears it can't help but want to come closer. Some fools of rivermen have been foolish and gone too near. They have been dashed to pieces on the rocks surrounding the Lorelei."

"Besides," said his friend, "we have to be careful of the castles along the Rhine. Robbers are said to live in many of them. They come out to capture ships for their cargoes."

"So you see, it's a very dangerous journey we are making," said Frederick, with a twinkle in his eye. The other raftsmen nodded.

Soon they finished eating the kettle of stew.

"The stew was good," said Jacob to Hans and Peter. The spicy food made him thirsty. He noticed that the men had no water for drinking. It gave him an idea.

"Frederick," he said loudly. "I know where there's a brook nearby. Its water tastes delicious. It tastes as if the juice from the valley's grapes were squeezed into it."

The raftsmen laughed at Jacob's exaggeration.

"Just the same," Frederick said, "the lad makes that water sound good." He licked his lips. "Just from hearing his story, I have a thirst for some of that delicious cool water."

"So do I," added the man beyond him.

Frederick tried to stand up. "Ouch!" he groaned and fell back. The other men laughed

at him. "I'm too stiff from working on the raft to fetch any water, though."

Jacob stood up slowly. He looked back toward the brook. He felt stiff himself.

"If I fetch the kettle full of water," he said, "would you take my letter?"

"You'll get water?" said Frederick. "It'll be a heavy load for you to carry, but then it's a long way to London, too." He nodded. "If you get the water, I'll carry the letter, somehow."

Jacob trudged back along the bank with the big empty kettle over his arm.

"We'll help," said Hans and Peter.

The raftsmen got their water.

When the boys returned home to Waldorf that night, Jacob knew his letter was on its way to his brother George in London at last.

Jacob Waits and Waits

Jacob sat between Hans and Peter at their graduation in 1777.

Schoolmaster Jeune stood before the graduates and their families. "You have all learned to read, write, and figure," he said to the graduates. "Also, I've taught you to play the flute. Now, go out into the world and show us what you can do."

Jacob felt uncomfortable in Mel's patched suit. He thought about the letter that George had written. There was a job for Jacob in London, but Poppa Astor had refused to let him go. "I must ask Poppa again," Jacob thought.

Jacob followed the other boys and girls out

of the church. The girls in pretty white dresses and the boys in black marched solemnly through a gathering of relatives.

Jacob heard someone call his name. He turned to see Ann Eve waving and Maria trying to hush the little girl. Jacob smiled toward his small sister and marched ahead.

When the graduates had marched down the road, the lines broke up. The girls cheered, and the boys hurrahed. Jacob thought how happy everyone looked. He smiled even though he didn't feel like smiling.

"We're grownups now," one girl said. "Isn't it nice! Our school days are over."

All the boys began talking about what they were going to do.

"I'm going to study at Heidelberg," one boy said. "I'm going to be a doctor."

"I'm going to be apprenticed to the blacksmith," said another.

Hans was happily showing off a new suit. His red hair was smoothed down neatly. "I'll soon be a baker," said Hans proudly.

"I'm going to start at the cartwright's tomorrow," said Peter.

Jacob moved away from the group of merrymakers. He looked for his family.

Poppa was standing alone by the pump. "I want to talk with you," said Jacob.

"What is it you want, Jacob?" asked Poppa Astor. He took his pipe from his mouth.

"Please let me go to London, Poppa. From there I could get to America."

Herr Astor shook his head. "Not yet, son. The British and Americans are still at war. I don't want you to go now."

"I can't go yet?" Jacob asked gloomily.

"George and Mel and Heinrich have gone off and been successful," said Poppa. "You probably wouldn't do as well as they have done."

"I'm sure I'd do as well," said Jacob.

"You must wait and have patience," said Poppa Astor. "Now is not the time."

For two years Jacob waited. He helped in the butcher shop—when there was business. He wheeled the cart full of meat about the village.

Finally one day Poppa called the family together. "I've decided to let Jacob go to London," he said.

"Hurrah," shouted Jacob. He threw his arms around his father.

Then Maria grabbed one of Jacob's arms, and Lisbet grabbed the other. Ann Eve held on, and the girls twirled Jacob round and round. Finally Jacob sat down out of breath.

"What will you do in America, Jacob?" asked Lisbet.

"I'm going to be a trader," said Jacob.

"Tell us more," begged Ann Eve.

"When I finally get to the New Land," Jacob

159

went on, "I'll trade far and wide. I'll see beautiful country, and I'd like to see some of those redskins and their villages.

The three girls gazed wide-eyed, as Jacob talked on and on.

A few mornings later he awoke early. He heard the village pigs grunting and the chickens cackling. Then he remembered that this was the day he would leave Waldorf. He climbed out of bed. Soon the rest of the family were awake.

"Must you leave so early in the morning?" asked Mama Astor.

"I have a long walk to the Rhine," explained Jacob to his mother.

Mama Astor found a large square piece of cloth. She packed Jacob's few clothes into it. She packed in a slice of ham she had saved especially for him and some fruit.

Jacob slid his flute in between the clothes. A crowd of villagers gathered to walk with

Jacob to the edge of Waldorf. Some of them asked him to carry letters to relatives in London. Many of Jacob's schoolmates came to see him off.

Peter came with a new wheel to show Jacob.

Hans brought a package. "Here's something for you to eat when you get hungry."

"It better not be a frog!" laughed Jacob. "I hope you're not up to your old tricks!"

The boys laughed at Jacob's teasing. Then Jacob said farewell to his family and to the crowd of villagers.

"We'll meet you in America sometime," many of the villagers called after him.

A few yards down the road, Jacob glanced back. The red tiled roofs of the cottages gleamed among the trees. The villagers waved.

As Jacob waved back, he thought of all the things he had learned in the village. "How little I know of the rest of the world!" he thought.

Then he swung his bag of clothes over his

shoulder, turned swiftly, and walked on toward the Rhine.

At the cobbled street, the group began to break up. "My stepson Jacob has big ideas," Mama Astor was saying proudly.

"He won't get as far as he wants to get," said a woman of the village.

"Don't worry about Jacob," said Schoolmaster Jeune. "He has a clear head and good sense between his ears. He'll do fine."

Jacob was walking on. The trees cast shadows on the road. The sun moved higher in the sky. He stopped and wiped his forehead. He switched the clothespack from one shoulder to the other.

After a while he rested on an old stump at the side of the road. He unwrapped the paper from Hans's package and found some rolls. As he munched the delicious rolls Hans had baked, Jacob thought about all that lay ahead of him.

Then he smoothed out the paper which Hans had wrapped around the rolls and wrote, "I, John Jacob Astor, resolve

> to be honest,
> to work hard, and
> not to gamble."

He folded the paper and put it in his pocket. He gathered up his clothes and went on, whistling. He was on his way at last.

That evening Jacob joined a rafting crew on the Rhine. The men sat about a campfire telling stories. Jacob entertained them with his flute.

In fourteen days the raft reached Holland. The master of the raft paid Jacob ten dollars for his work. Jacob looked at his ten dollars. It was more money than he had ever seen. "It's a fortune!" he said.

He took a boat over to England.

Several days later in London Jacob knocked

on the door of George's house. A friendly-looking woman opened the door. Then Jacob saw his brother George behind her.

"Come in, Jacob. Come in. This is my wife, Elizabeth," said George.

Jacob greeted his brother and sister-in-law. The brothers stood back to look at one another. George looked older now. He had his own flute and piano factory and his own family.

"Have something to eat, Jacob," said Elizabeth. She brought some rolls and tea.

As they ate, Jacob told George how thankful he was to have a job in his factory. "I want to earn money so I can start out as a trader in North America."

George looked up from his cup and said, "You'll need more than money. You'll need peaceful conditions in America."

"The war's over," said Jacob.

"The treaty's not signed," said George. "You

ought to wait for that, if you expect to do much business trading."

"Get off to bed now," said Elizabeth. "You will have to be up bright and early in the morning, if you want to go to the factory."

"Let Jacob sleep late tomorrow, to rest after his journey," said George, leaning back in his chair. "He's come a long way."

"No," said Jacob. "I want to start work right away. I'll be at work in the flute factory directly in the morning."

To America

ONE DAY a few weeks later Jacob was strolling through London with George and Elizabeth and their family.

Jacob glanced at a man up ahead. "What kind of hat is that man wearing?" asked Jacob. He was used to seeing three-cornered hats. This hat was high, with a brim about the bottom.

"It's strange-looking, all right," said George. "They're called 'top hats,' because they stick up."

"They look like cans turned upside down," said Elizabeth.

The children laughed at the hat.

"I think it's a handsome hat," said Jacob. "See

how dignified and tall the man looks. The material looks soft and glossy."

"It's beaver skin," said George. "Top hats like that are coming into fashion."

As they strolled on, Jacob listened to the English people talking. "How will I ever learn to speak English well?" he said. "I want to know it well for trading in America. How can I trade with people if I don't know their language?"

"You will learn it easily," said Elizabeth, "but you must twist your tongue differently from when you are speaking German. Stick out your tongue when you say 'they.' Then you won't pronounce it 'dey.'"

Jacob tried twisting his tongue. He felt foolish sticking out his tongue, but he was pleased when "they" came out, instead of "dey."

"Ha! Ha!" laughed his nephew George Peter.

Jacob reached down and tickled his young nephew in the ribs.

In a few weeks Jacob was able to make people understand him when he spoke English. He worked hard listening to people, so he would know many English words. Until the end of his life, however, he often said "dey" instead of pronouncing it "they."

Jacob always listened eagerly to news about America and the progress of the war.

One day in 1783 Jacob, a young man now, looked out the window of the factory. People were shouting and dancing about the streets.

"The war's over" said the worker beside Jacob. "The peace treaty's been signed. Mr. Benjamin Franklin has signed the peace treaty!"

"The war's over! HURRAH!" shouted Jacob as he hurried out into the streets.

Everyone was shouting and dancing. A man threw his hat high into the air. It skittered sideways and landed at Jacob's feet. He picked it up and handed it back to the man.

"Thanks," said the man. "That's an expensive hat. I'm glad to have it returned."

"It's made of beaver skin," isn't it?" said Jacob.

The man nodded. "Beaver skins ar expensive. They come all the way from America."

That evening after the excitement, Jacob returned to his room in George's house. He counted his savings. He had sent part of his earnings back to Waldorf. Now there were only fifteen gold coins left. It seemed hardly enough to get to America. "I must not wait any longer," Jacob thought to himself. "I must go to America, now!"

Jacob went downstairs to the supper table. "George," he said, "I want to buy seven new flutes from you."

"Seven at once!" said George in surprise.

Jacob nodded.

"Are you going to play them all in your mouth at the same time, Uncle Jacob?" asked young George Peter with a giggle.

170

Jacob smiled and said, "Of course not. I've decided to leave for America. I'm going to take the flutes with me. I'll trade them when I arrive there. I hope to make a profit."

"Do you think the people in America want flutes?" asked Elizabeth. "They are so busy just making a living."

"People need pleasure, as well as food and clothing," answered Jacob. "If I have luck trading these flutes, I'll send for more."

In the morning Jacob went to the tailor's shop.

"I want a new suit," Jacob told the tailor. "I want to look fine when I make my way to America." At last he could wear a suit that hadn't belonged to one older brother or another.

"Would you like a fine beaver hat, too?" asked the tailor. "Everyone is wearing top hats these days. The fur comes from America."

Jacob ran his hand over the glossy, soft beaver skin on the tailor's counter. "I can't afford a beaver top hat," he said. He hoped the money left would take him to America.

In November, 1783, the docks in Bristol, England, were noisy with activity. Jacob hurried along the wharf with the flutes, and his new suit, and a few gold coins. Shipmasts towered over his head, and people hurried about.

"Get out of the way!" a voice called.

Jacob jumped back. A barrel rolled down a gangplank and continued past him. "Products from America," he heard someone say.

Jacob went on. He found a hull with *North Carolina* painted across it. Slinging the bag of flutes over his shoulder, he approached the captain, a big man with weather-beaten cheeks.

"How much for a place in steerage?" asked Jacob. He held his breath.

"Five guineas," replied Captain Jacob Stout.

Jacob took out five guineas from his pocket. He would only have five guineas left. "I'll pay that much if you'll supply me with food for the voyage," he bargained.

Captain Stout nodded. "You can have salt beef and biscuit until we get to America," he said. "Go on board."

Proudly, Jacob walked up the gangplank. It looked as if he would get to America at last.

He climbed down below the deck. It was dark and damp, and he had a hard time finding his bunk. He stuffed his belongings beneath the mattress and stretched out on his bunk.

"What's in that long bag?" asked a voice behind him.

It was a voice with a German accent. Jacob turned to the friendly face. He was happy he would be able to talk a little German on the voyage, even though he knew English now.

Rudolph, the German, was on his way back to America. "I bought furs in the wilderness," he explained to Jacob. "I brought them to London, and I made a good profit on them. Hat makers are all eager to get American furs."

That night, when the ship put out to sea, Jacob lay in his bunk. As the ship swayed, he thought about where he was going. He wondered about all the things he would do.

One day he sat on the deck with Rudolph. The sea was rough. Jacob bit into one of the hard biscuits and ate a piece of salt beef. He wished he had some good sausage and pumpernickel.

"Look at those gentlemen," said Rudolph, pointing to some men on the quarter-deck.

"Who are they?" asked Jacob.

"They're officers of the Hudson's Bay Company," answered Rudolph.

Jacob could hear the men talking about fur and Indians.

"What's the Hudson's Bay Company?" he asked Rudolph, the German.

"It's an English company," replied Rudolph.

"It has trading forts, and trades with the Indians for furs."

Jacob's eyes opened wide. "Then they have large companies in America, like the lumbering company on the Rhine."

Rudolph nodded and said, "The Hudson's Bay Company controls much of the fur trade, even the fur trade in the land west of the Mississippi."

"The United States ought to control the fur trade, too."

After that, whenever Jacob saw the Hudson's Bay officers on deck, he wondered if there was a place for him in the fur business, too.

By January, 1784, the *North Carolina* reached Chesapeake Bay. Jacob gazed out at the floating ice. "One more day, and we'll be in America!" he thought excitedly.

By morning, the wind had died down, and the weather was colder. The ship's hull was frozen tightly in ice.

The Hudson's Bay Company officers walked over the ice and hired a coach into Baltimore. Jacob stayed on board ship and lived on salt beef and biscuit. The more he ate of this food, the less he liked it.

The ice remained all through February. The food was soon rationed. Finally at the end of March, Jacob had waited long enough. Then, he, too, set on foot across the ice to Baltimore. He arrived in America at last.

From Baltimore he went on to New York City. There he set out to find the home of his brother Heinrich and his famliy.

With his flutes and his new suit, Jacob walked about New York City. It was only a small city then. Jacob looked at the ships in the harbor. He walked up the cobblestones of Broadway and admired the broad tulip trees and the stately maple trees.

Everywhere, people were doing things.

Everywhere, Jacob saw top hats made of beaver skin. He hurried on.

He had never seen so many busy people. His feet moved faster. "This is the land of opportunity, for sure!" he thought to himself. He went on with a bounce in his step.

Finally Jacob found his brother's house. Heinrich was still fat and jolly. His wife was young and pretty.

"Ah, Jacob," said Heinrich, "At last you've come. My butchering trade is growing, and I can certainly use you in my business."

Jacob shook his head. "I'm not going to be a butcher," he said.

Jacob worked for a few weeks for a baker and finally found a job with a furrier. He worked hard beating furs so they would stay in good condition while in storage.

"You're a fast worker, Jacob," said his employer one day. "You work hard, and you keep your eyes open. You can recognize all the different kinds of fur now. Would you like to go out and buy furs for me, instead of working in the warehouse?"

"I certainly would," said Jacob.

In the fall of 1785 Jacob married Sarah Todd and soon became a fur trader himself.

Jacob and Sarah opened a store at 81 Queen Street. Sarah worked as hard as Jacob. She kept the store where she sold flutes from George's factory in London, while Jacob attended to his fur business. At the store she also sold furs.

Later on Jacob and Sarah moved to 40 Little Dock Street where they opened another shop.

In this time Jacob and Sarah also raised five children: Magdalen, John Jacob, Jr., William, Dorothea, and Eliza. In Sarah's store she sold flutes from George's factory in London. But the main thing she sold was furs.

"Father, this will make a fine fur hat," said

young William one day to Jacob. The baby Dorothea grabbed at a fur, too, and Jacob scooped it away from her. He rubbed a fur on her cheek, and she laughed gleefully.

"May I go to Montreal with you on your next trip, Father?" begged Magdalen, the oldest child. "Please let me go."

"Yes, daughter," said Jacob, "but first I am going to make a trip into western New York."

In a few weeks, he was tramping through the forests with a pack of trade goods on his back. He turned into an Indian village.

The Oneida Indian chief was surprised when Jacob spoke to him in the Oneida language. Jacob had taught himself the Indian languages, for he thought a good trader should speak the language of his customer.

After the Indian traded a few furs for some of the items Jacob brought, they sat about the campfire and talked.

Jacob brought out his flute and played for the Indians. The Indians watched him with amazement. Then they brought out some of their own instruments and entertained him.

Jacob put the glossy furs into his pack and tramped back to New York City with the heavy load on his back. He could hardly wait to see see Sarah and the children again.

"Father's home!" said William running up Little Dock Street. He took the heavy pack and dragged it home with the help of Magdalen.

In the back room, Sarah looked over the furs. She was good at judging their quality.

The children listened with interest, as Jacob told about his trip.

The next time he went on a trading trip to Montreal, he took Magdalen with him.

Often he thought of the land west of the Mississippi and west of the Rockies. He knew it was land rich in furs. In Montreal he heard talk about England's control of the fur trade in the West. It made him angry.

Jacob's fur trading business grew. He bought much land in New York City. The fur trade in the West still interested him. "I must do something," Jacob often thought. At last he had a plan to open up the fur trade in the West for the United States.

World Trader

ONE DAY in 1808 President Thomas Jefferson was sitting at his desk. He held a letter out to his Secretary of War, General Henry Dearborn.

"I have heard of this man, John Jacob Astor," said the President. "Tell me more, General Dearborn. What do you know about him?"

"John Jacob Astor is a wealthy New York merchant," said General Dearborn. "His trade is mostly in furs. He obtains most of his furs from Montreal."

President Jefferson sighed. "That is the trouble," he said. "The United States should have its own fur trade. Other countries control the fur trade in the West. Some day the Far West should be a part of the United States, but it will never be, if we don't have our own traders there."

"What can be done, Mr. President?" asked General Dearborn.

President Jefferson glanced down at the letter. Then his face brightened. "Astor has written me," he said. "He has a plan to develop the fur trade in the West. He wants to start an American fur company. He wants to build trading forts all along the Missouri River and farther on into Oregon territory. I'm going to approve his plan. Our traders will get to the West."

Sarah and Jacob and their children rejoiced when they were informed of the President's approval of the plans for the new trading posts.

Jacob sent two expeditions out to Oregon. He sent one ship, the *Tonquin*, around South America and up the Pacific Coast. The men of the *Tonquin* built a trading fort at the mouth of

184

the Columbia River, on land that is now the state of Oregon. They called it Fort Astoria.

Now the flag of the United States flew on the Pacific Coast. Everyone in the United States began talking about the Far West. "That land ought to be part of the United States," people were saying. "We have settlers there."

Jacob sent another expedition to Oregon by land. On the way, this group met Daniel Boone.

Daniel talked to members of the expedition around a campfire. "I'd join your group and go on with you," said Daniel Boone, "if I weren't getting too old."

In New York City Jacob sat on his porch at his big house on Broadway. On a map, he showed his children the routes of his expeditions to Oregon. He showed Heinrich and his sisters, too.

By now, Catherine and Lisbet and Ann Eve had come to the United States. Back in Waldorf Maria was married. Mama Astor had died. Herr Astor was still alive. He was no longer poor, for his four successful sons sent him money. Jacob was the most successful of them all.

Everything did not work out for Jacob, however. One day a few years later Sarah and the children were all sad. "Your plan to develop the fur trade in the Far West has failed," said Sarah. "Jacob, what are you going to do now?"

Jacob shrugged his shoulders. The War of 1812 had wrecked his plans in Oregon. "I'm sorry about the failure," said Jacob, "but it's foolish to cry over failures. I'm going to develop the fur trade in the land about the Mississippi, and I have other plans."

Eliza Astor looked over her father's shoulder. He had a map spread out on the table. "What are all those pins for?" she asked.

"They stand for ships that I have bought," said Jacob. "A trader needs ships." He pointed to the different pins.

"Here in New York are the *Enterprise*, the *Hannibal*, and my brig *Seneca*. On the coast of France are the *Fingal* and the *Boxer*." Then he pointed to several more.

"Where are you going to send those ships?" Eliza asked her grandfather.

"I'm going to develop the trade with China," said Jacob.

"Trade with China!" said Eliza. "What will you trade with China?"

"The people of this country like many things from China. They like the beautiful willowware china dishes. They like tea and spices and silks."

"And what do the Chinese want?"

"They want furs to make into fur cloaks."

Sarah threw up her hands. "If one plan fails for you, Jacob, you never brood," she said. "You just start on another plan."

"Grandpa's coming!" the little girl called. She pressed her nose against the shiny glass window. It was 1832, and the grandchildren were waiting in the Astor mansion.

"Let me see! I can't see!" shouted the many little boys and girls in back of the window.

"I think someone's with him," shouted another girl. "I wonder who he is."

188

"Patience, children. Patience. Don't push so," said Sarah Astor, smoothing back her grey hair. She smiled. "He'll be here in a minute—and spoiling the lot of you."

"Grandpa's coach is here now!" shouted a sturdy boy. The children stared out at Jacob Astor's fine yellow coach. Passersby on the street stopped to admire it, also.

"Is that really Mr. Astor, the fur merchant?" asked a man on the street.

"He is the richest man in the United States," said another. "He owns much of the land of New York City."

"He looks like any ordinary person," said a third. John Jacob Astor wore plain clothes.

From inside the house, the grandchildren stared at the horses. "Look at the shiny coats of those horses," said a boy. He knew how his Grandpa loved his horses. He thought how on nice days, his Grandpa went horseback riding.

One very small boy looked at the horses and went galloping about the room. "Giddap! Giddap!" the little boy shouted. He put his head down and charged.

When the richest man in the United States walked into the front door, the little boy galloped straight into him.

"Oh, Grandpa!" said the other children.

John Jacob Astor stood back in surprise. Then the richest man in the United States laughed a deep laugh and picked up the little grandson. "So, so," he said.

The man with him was a pianist, who played any tune the children asked for. John Jacob Astor sang them a song about the Rhine, and he showed the children his old flute.

As the children chattered, John Jacob Astor glanced across the room at Sarah and smiled.

"Tell us about your fur trader days, Grandpa!" begged the children.

190

"Tell us about when you were a little boy in Germany," begged another child.

"Tell us about the ships you sent to China and all over the world," begged a third child.

Mr. Astor's eyes twinkled. He told the children stories. He played his flute, too.

Later his friend Mr. Washington Irving came in. The children knew Mr. Irving had written the famous stories about Ichabod Crane and Rip Van Winkle.

With his beloved family about him, at that moment, the richest man in the United States was also the happiest man in the United States.

Years later something else made John Jacob Astor joyful. News came from Washington. It was 1846 and President James K. Polk declared that Oregon had become part of the territory of the United States. How pleased Mr. Astor was about that. His friend Washington Irving was pleased, too. In 1836 Mr. Irving had written a book called *Astoria* about the plan to develop the fur trade in Oregon.

"My Astoria plan didn't fail completely," said John Jacob Astor.

"No," said Washington Irving. "After your venture, others were brave enough to settle there. That's why it became part of the United States. If it hadn't been for your 'failure,' the United States would look very different now."

More About This Book

WHEN JOHN JACOB ASTOR LIVED

1763 JOHN JACOB ASTOR WAS BORN IN WALDORF, GERMANY, JULY 17.

There were thirteen English colonies in North America.

The French and Indian War ended.

Pontiac led an unsuccessful Indian uprising.

The population of the thirteen colonies in America was about 2,500,000.

1764-
1779 JACOB GREW UP IN WALDORF.

The Stamp Act was passed, 1765.

Daniel Boone first went to Kentucky, 1769.

The Boston Massacre occurred, 1770.

The "Boston Tea Party" took place, 1773.

The first battle of the Revolutionary War was fought at Lexington, Massachusetts, 1775.

The Declaration of Independence was signed, 1776.

General Burgoyne surrendered, 1777.

| 1780- | JACOB WORKED IN ENGLAND IN HIS BROTHER |
| 1783 | GEORGE'S FLUTE FACTORY. |

Cornwallis surrendered at Yorktown, 1781.

The peace treaty with England was signed, ending the Revolutionary War, 1783.

| 1784- | JACOB ARRIVED IN AMERICA AND ENGAGED IN |
| 1810 | FUR TRADING. |

The Constitutional Convention met to frame the United States Constitution, 1787.

The Northwest Territory was established, 1787.

George Washington became the first president, 1797.

Captain Robert Gray discovered the Columbia River, 1792.

Lewis and Clark explored the Northwest, 1804-1806.

| 1811- | JACOB EXPANDED HIS TRADING TO THE WEST |
| 1826 | AND CHINA. |

The War of 1812 was fought, 1812-1815.

"The Star-Spangled Banner" was written, 1814.

The Monroe Doctrine was issued, 1823.

The Erie Canal was completed, 1825.

194

1827-
1847 JACOB LIVED IN RETIREMENT.

American settlers reached Oregon, 1836.

Elias Howe invented the sewing machine, 1846.

The United States acquired the Oregon Territory south of the forty-ninth parallel, 1846.

1848 JOHN JACOB ASTOR DIED IN HIS HOME IN NEW YORK CITY, MARCH 29.

There were twenty-nine states in the Union.

James K. Polk was President.

The population of the country was about 21,900,000.

DO YOU REMEMBER?

1. About when and where was Jacob born?

2. Where did Jacob go to school?

3. Who was his schoolteacher?

4. Who were Jacob's playmates?

5. How many brothers and sisters did Jacob have?

6. In what trade was Jacob's father engaged?

7. What river was near Jacob's home?

8. What instrument did Jacob learn to play?

9. What was Jacob's ambition?

10. What was the "Boston Massacre"?

11. Where did Jacob and his playmates like to play?

12. What was the story of the Lorelie?

13. What was the magic from America that the students traded with Jacob?

14. How was meat cured in Jacob's day?

15. What did Jacob resolve when he left Waldorf?

16. How did Jacob get to England?

17. What was the name of the ship that brought Jacob to America?

18. What did Jacob take with him to America?

IT'S FUN TO LOOK UP THESE THINGS

1. Where is the Rhine River? Where is the Columbia River?

2. What Indian tribes were known as the "Five Nations"?

3. Who were the following people and why are they remembered today: Meriwether Lewis, William Clark, Jim Bridger, Daniel Boone, Marcus Whitman, Washington Irving?

4. What was the life of a fur trader like?

5. Why did the colonists want their freedom from England?

6. What were some of the causes of the War of 1812?

7. Who were some of the early settlers of the Oregon Country?

8. What items were used by fur traders to trade with the Indians?

9. What are the stories of Ichabod Crane and Rip Van Winkle?

INTERESTING THINGS YOU CAN DO

1. Read about the Lewis and Clark expedition and give a report to the class.

2. Construct a trading post such as the one founded at Fort Astoria. Twigs can be used for the logs.

3. Make a map showing the places where John Jacob Astor carried on his trading.

4. Make a collection of pictures of the types of ships that carried on the China trade.

5. Prepare a report on the influence of the fur traders in the settlement of the United States.

OTHER BOOKS YOU MAY ENJOY READING

Albert Einstein: Boy Mathematician, Marie Hammontree. Trade and School Editions, Bobbs-Merrill.

Daniel Boone: Boy Hunter, Augusta Stevenson. Trade and School Editions, Bobbs-Merrill.

Empire of Fur, August Derleth. Trade Edition, Dutton. School Edition, American Book Company.

George Washington's World, Genevieve Foster. Scribner's.

Hudson's Bay Company, The, Richard Morenus. Trade Edition, Random House. School Edition, Hale.

Kateri Tekakwitha, Mohawk Maid, Evelyn M. Brown. Farrar, Straus and Cudahy.

Trappers and Traders of the Far West, James Daugherty. Trade Edition, Random House. School Edition, Hale.

INTERESTING WORDS IN THIS BOOK

apprenticed (ă prĕn′ tĭst) : arranged to work for a certain length of time to learn a trade

axle (ăk′ s'l) : pin or rod on which a wheel revolves

blacksmith (blăk′ smĭth′) : man who forges iron

198

boar (bōr) : wild hog

brig (brĭg) : two-masted ship with square sails

cartwright (kärt′ rīt′) : man who makes or repairs carts or wagons

cobblestone (kŏb′ 'l stōn′) : round stone used in paving a street

expedition (ĕks′ pė dĭsh′ ŭn) : journey undertaken for some definite purpose or reason

flutist (flōot′ ĭst) : person who plays the flute

hull (hŭl) : body of a ship

industry (ĭn′ dŭs trĭ) : business

injustice (ĭn jŭs′ tĭs) : unjust act; a wrong

lanky (lăngk′ ĭ) : tall and thin

logging (lŏg′ ing) : business of cutting trees, making them into logs, and getting the logs to market

massacre (măs′ à kẽr) : violent killing of a number of people

mischievous (mĭs′ chĭ vŭs) : causing trouble

mound (mound) : hill

pillar (pĭl′ẽr) : column

procession (prȯ sĕsh′ ŭn) : group of persons marching in an orderly manner

prow (prou) : forward part of a ship

pumpernickel (pŭm′ pẽr nĭk′ ′l) : coarse bread made of rye

rationed (răsh′ ŭnd) : supplied in fixed daily amounts

sawhorse (sô′ hôrs′) : rack on which wood is laid for sawing by hand

sawmill (sô′ mĭl′) : machine for sawing logs

scythe (sīth) : instrument with long curving blade used for cutting grain by hand

smokehouse (smōk′ hous′) : building where meat or fish is exposed to dense smoke

smoldering (smōl′ dẽr ing) : burning and smoking without a flame

spit (spĭt) : slender, pointed iron rod for holding meat over a fire

suitor (sūt′ ẽr) : one who wants to marry

trader (trād′ ẽr) : one who exchanges one piece of goods for another; a merchant

tusk (tŭsk) : long large tooth

vision (vizh′ ŭn) : foresight

whirlpool (hwûrl′ pōol′) : water moving rapidly in a circle and producing a place in the center into which floating objects may be drawn

willowware (wĭl′ ȯ wâr′) : blue dishes from China

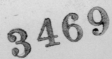